Science and the Book of Mormon

CURELOMS, CUMOMS, HORSES AND MORE

By

Wade E. Miller

Published by KCT & Associates
30092 Alicia Parkway, Laguna Niguel, CA 92677

Cover designed by Rod Laverne

ISBN
Printed in the United States of America

Dedication

To my great-great-grandfather, Charles W. Penrose, former member of the LDS Church's First Presidency, who was largely responsible for the Pronunciation Guide to the Book of Mormon.

Acknowledgments

Very deep appreciation is expressed to the people who took much time to critically review the manuscript for this book. Their comments helped to improve it. The author alone, however, is responsible for any errors of commission or omission. Those who kindly reviewed the manuscript are Duane E. Jeffery and Wilford M. Hess, both biology professors at Brigham Young University (BYU), Dale E. Miller, emeritus General Authority of the Church of Jesus Christ of Latter-day Saints, Marja-Leena Rogers, writer and former administrative assistant in the Geology Department at BYU, Norman C. Davis, Attorney at Law, Santa Ana, California. I also would like to thank my wife, Patricia F. Miller, who provided loving patience and support throughout the research and writing of this book.

Gratitude and special thanks are extended to Marja-Leena Rogers who helped gather and provide needed information, and to John L. Sorenson, emeritus professor of archaeology, and Richard O. Jensen, chief science librarian, both of BYU, who also supplied desired data. Keith Terry, of MWP Media Publishers, Laguna Niguel, California, is thanked for help at various stages in the publication of this book.

Table of Contents

Introduction

Certainly the prophets who wrote their records that are included in the Book of Mormon, never intended that the purpose be one of providing scientific information. This Book is meant to be a witness of Christ, as well as one that teaches His doctrines. Its extended title emphasizes that Jesus Christ is the central figure – "The Book of Mormon: Another Testament of Jesus Christ." As former Latter-day Saint Church president, Ezra Taft Benson declared, "It is the keystone of our religion." (Ensign, January, 1992, p. 2)

Although it was not intended to be a record of scientific information, the Book of Mormon does include a number of statements that bear on this subject. In both First and Third Nephi it's related that earthquakes would (did) occur with portions of the earth being broken up, of mountains tumbling down, and of severe storms wreaking havoc on the land. (1 Nephi 12:4; 3 Nephi 8:6-18) When it's written in the Old Testament that the sun stood still (Joshua 10:13), the Book of Mormon prophet Helaman related that, "... according to his [God's] word the earth goeth back, and it appeareth unto man that the sun standeth still." (Helaman 12:15) These are only a couple of events mentioned that come under the purview of science. Numerous others can be found within the Book of Mormon, many of which are included in the present book.

It should be mentioned here that many able scholars have written about the Book of Mormon from a variety of perspectives, including scientific ones. I will be referring to some of these works. My own scientific background in paleontology and geology gives me some different insights that are elaborated upon in this book.

Both the Jaredites and Nephites recorded implements and materials that they used, crops they grew, and animals with which they were familiar. All this has scientific bearing. However, a number of people have taken many of these items and tried to use them to "prove" that the Book of Mormon could not be true. Statements these people have used to refute the Book of Mormon go something like this: "Peoples of the Book of Mormon could not have known about steel; they would not have had linen and silk or some of the grains mentioned; elephants were not present; there were no horses in America before the time of Columbus when Spaniards introduced them," and so forth. This book demonstrates that these and other objections are no longer scientifically valid. Scientific evidences that substantiate the Book of Mormon were clearly not known to Joseph Smith at the time he translated the golden plates.

While the Book of Mormon does not rely on science to verify its authenticity, it is good to know that rather than disparaging the Book, science actually supports it. Many evidences for this are provided in the chapters that follow. Keep in mind, too, that just because a given evidence has not yet been found, does not mean it never will. Paleontologists and archaeologists have a saying, "absence of evidence is not evidence of absence."

1

Authenticity of the Book of Mormon

It surprised me when I learned that apparently many thousands of people have contacted the Smithsonian Institution, asking whether they had information confirming or refuting the authenticity of the Book of Mormon. Those asking have been both members and non-members of the Church of Jesus Christ of Latter-day Saints. Most of the questions asked recently are of an archeological or anthropological nature. Examples of these questions are: Could Native Americans have arrived in America by boat? Were they from the Middle East? Did they really possess the ability to make steel and glass? Did they have linen and silk? Were there actually horses in America when they arrived? The list goes on.

The head of the Smithsonian's Anthropology Outreach Office used to routinely send out a formal written response of several pages to those requesting information regarding scientific aspects of the Book of Mormon. Currently this office provides a shorter version that can be obtained by contacting them. In the lengthy 1979 version of their official statement, which was used for many years, they would essentially refute Book of Mormon claims of an archeological or anthropological nature.

Examples given in their earlier statement are: "The physical type of the American Indian is basically Mongoloid in origin." "The first people to reach North America by sea were the Norse around 1000 A.D." "None of the Old World domesticated food plants or animals (except the dog) were in the Americas before the arrival of the Spaniards." "Camels and horses were in the Americas with the bison, mammoth, and mastodon, but all these animals became extinct around 10,000 years ago." "Items such as iron, steel, glass, and silk were not in the New World before 1492." I wrote to the Anthropological Outreach Office at the Smithsonian Institution requesting any current statement that they had regarding these issues concerning the Book of Mormon. The following is a quote of the response that I received:

"This letter from the Smithsonian's Department of Anthropology is in response to your inquiry regarding the Book of Mormon. The Smithsonian considers the Book of Mormon a religious document and not a scientific guide. The Smithsonian Institution has never used it in archaeological research and has found no archaeological evidence to support its claims." Dated February 15, 2006.

This last, more recent statement, is somewhat "toned down" from the earlier ones. But it certainly is not an endorsement for the Book of Mormon. John L. Sorenson, highly respected archaeologist at Brigham Young University, with many scholarly works on Mesoamerica, responded to the Smithsonian pointing out their many mistakes on earlier statements as described above (2007, Pers. Comm.).

This is probably one good reason why the Smithsonian's Anthropology Outreach Office greatly shortened their response to inquires about the Book of Mormon. Scientific finds over the past three decades have also done much to cause the Smithsonian Institution to back away from their earlier statements critical of Book of Mormon claims. In fairness to those responsible for the Smithsonian statements, they now do include a list of publications which have a bearing on Book of Mormon archaeology. Some of the references they provide give favorable reports.

The intent of this book is to add to the body of knowledge relating to science in the Book of Mormon using my paleontological and geological background. At some point I realized that my own study and research could provide information helpful in answering questions, and hopefully alleviating some doubts. I will discuss the animals mentioned in the Book of Mormon in greater depth than other scientific aspects. These other aspects which have caused concern will only be briefly discussed as others have treated them at length.

2

Book of Mormon Lands

Since the Book of Mormon was first published in 1830, critics have claimed that it could not be true for a variety of reasons. Many of these reasons that have been continually brought out over the years relate to items people have said were not in the New World before the Spaniards arrived. Items[1] commonly named include the existence of steel, glass, linen, silk, barley, wheat, and diverse species of animals including the horse. Several LDS and other scholars have addressed these and other criticisms. Some of this information is available on the internet. While the work of all these scholars has benefitted me, the extensive research done by Hugh Nibley and John L. Sorenson, both former professors at Brigham Young University, has proven to be especially enlightening.

Their historical, cultural, and archeological studies have provided a number of important insights into the peoples of the Book of Mormon. In my first few readings of this sacred book I felt that the history of the Jaredites and the Nephites took place in both North and South America - or at least North and Central America. The LDS Church has never made an official statement on where the Book of Mormon peoples lived. It occurred to me some years ago, however, that the Hill Cumorah in the state of New

---

[1] These items come to us as translated words from another language. And translations of words in the scriptures are basically all that we have when we read them. There must be a number of times in which we read a given word and come to a different understanding than what was originally meant by the author. Because of this we might not interpret a given word correctly. I think that this holds true for some of the materials, plants and animals spoken of in the Book of Mormon. This should be kept in mind with each of the items discussed in this book.

York could be a renamed hill from the original one that was located in Mesoamerica (Others of course have reached this same conclusion). It was possibly here that Moroni first hid the gold plates that were later moved, and then translated by Joseph Smith to become the Book of Mormon. My opinion of where the Book of Mormon lands actually were has been changed due to the work of several LDS scholars.

One scholar mentioned previously, John L. Sorenson, has provided much evidence to show that the region was probably relatively small. According to him it did not encompass the Americas. He believes that the area of record was just what is now southern Mexico and Guatemala, part of Mesoamerica (Sorenson, 1985, p. 37; 2002, p. 273). As should be expected, though, even among LDS scholars, there are differences of opinion. BYU archaeologist, Raymond T. Matheny, has stated that there is presently insufficient evidence to accurately determine how extensive Book of Mormon lands were. (2008, Pers. Comm.). It could be that the main story of Book of Mormon prophets and their record keeping was in Mesoamerica, but that subsequently, when records were no longer kept, the remaining people dispersed throughout the Americas.

In my opinion there seems to be support for favoring Sorenson's view that Book of Mormon lands probably were part of Mesoamerica. (1985, pp. 14, 37) The Jaredite people mainly would have lived here as well. Certainly there is evidence indicating that they lived somewhere close, or within, what later became Nephite and Lamanite lands. As discussed in the Book of Mosiah (8:7-11), King Limhi sent 43 of his people to locate the land of Zarahemla. Rather than finding this land, though, they discovered a land containing ruins of buildings, one covered with bones of men and beasts, and weapons of war. Records in the form of 24 gold plates holding a history of this people (see the Book of Ether in the Book of Mormon) were also found. It therefore seems that the center of Jaredite civilization must have been close to that of the later Nephites and Lamanites. In fact it was prophesied by Ether to King Coriantumr that another people would receive his land for their inheritance. (Ether 13:21) Also, Moroni recorded that the army of Coriantumr pitched their tents by the hill Ramah, ("… the same hill where my father Mormon did hide up the records unto the Lord, which were sacred." (Ether 15:11)

Another evidence for my believing that the land of the Jaredites, Nephites and Lamanites was more likely in Mesoamerica, rather than what is now the eastern part of the United States, has to do with climate and geology. This is despite the fact that the Hill Cumorah[2] as now recognized is in the state of New York. Nowhere in the Book of Mormon is cold weather or snow mentioned. Brigham Young University geology professor, Bart Kowallis, made a good case for the natural disasters occurring among the Nephites and Lamanites, just prior to the resurrected Christ's appearance, being mainly due to volcanic activity. (Kowallis,1998). I concur with his view that the cause of these disasters, written in 3 Nephi in the Book of Mormon, were of volcanic origin. Mesoamerica even today is a region prone to violent volcanic activity. This activity is often coupled with earthquakes and storms. Geologists Robert H. Dott and Roger L. Batten said, "One of the most volcanically active regions in the World is Central America." (1988, p. 4) What is now eastern North America, including New York of course, has not experienced volcanic activity for many, many, millions of years. It is a geologically stable region.

---

[2] This same name, "Cumorah," was previously applied to a hill (and land) indicated by the prophet Mormon. He hid the records on gold plates there. (Mormon 6:6)

3

Steel and Glass in
the Book of Mormon

When I first read the Book of Mormon I was intrigued that Nephi had a steel bow. It did seem like an anachronism. (My own interest in bows and arrows began when my uncle very carefully made ones of wood for me when I was a boy. So this got my attention). Later I learned that this bow of Nephi caused concern for many people. Many claimed that steel wasn't known in 600 B.C.

These critics must not have read the Old Testament, at least not very carefully, as it reveals something about steel. In Samuel it reads, "He teacheth my hand to war; so that a bow of steel is broken by mine arms." (2 Samuel 22:35). It seems ironic that when steel is mentioned in 1 Nephi it's stated, "And it came to pass that as I, Nephi, went forth to slay food, behold, I did break my bow, which was made of fine steel...." (1 Nephi 16:18). Since Samuel the prophet of the Old Testament lived at the time of David, this would have been approximately 1000 B.C. His mention of steel predates Nephi by roughly 400 years.

Perhaps a more serious objection to steel being in the New World before Columbus is that mentioned in the Jaredite record within the Book of Mormon. The recorded statement is, "Wherefore, he [Shule] came to the hill Ephraim, and did molten out of the hill, and made swords out of steel ..." (Ether 7:9). It is not known exactly when Shule lived, but he was the great-grandson of Jared. As a very rough approximation, this would have been about 2100 B.C. Did the Jaredites invent steel after coming to the New World, or did they bring a knowledge of this metal with them from the Old? I don't know. But I do know, along with most people, that steel is a combination of iron and carbon.

Whether steel is low or high grade depends on a number of factors, including the quality of materials used, technique, and process involved. Nephi said that his bow was made of fine steel. No mention is made of the quality of the steel of Shule's swords (Ether 7:9). Now, when was the first steel produced, and by whom? There is much conflicting information about this.

One serious problem is that iron and steel rust, so ancient evidences of these metals are rare. It seems probable, though, that since iron has been known in the form of iron-nickel meteorites from ancient times that man worked with it. A Mesopotamian knife blade of iron, dated to the 28th Century B.C. was reported in a work by Hugh Nibley (1988, p. 214). He also stated that iron beads from Egypt had been dated to about 3500 B.C. (1988, p. 215). A low grade of steel could be produced from molten iron mixed with the coals of a fire. This might have been done, if only accidentally, by ancient peoples independently in various parts of the world. Metallurgist R. J. Forbes commented, "It is doubtful whether the ancients knew any direct method of producing steel, but they produced it accidentally when they treated suitable ores." (1950, p. 409). For me there is no problem in believing that the Jaredites and Nephites both used steel. Common sense alone allows for this. However, to date no archaeological evidence has yet been found showing the manufacture of steel among the Jaredites or Nephites. Such evidence, though, might yet be discovered.

Glass is another of the items that Book of Mormon critics have used to discount the Book, stating that glass was not present in the Americas before the time of Columbus. Actually, glass is not mentioned as being in the New World by either the Jaredites or Nephites. Its mention only comes in the repeating of a chapter of

Isaiah in 2 Nephi. "The glasses, and the fine linen, and the hoods, and the vails." (Isaiah 3:23; 2 Nephi 13:23).

The only other place in the Book of Mormon where I could find a mention of glass is in the Book of Ether. Here it's stated that the brother of Jared, "... did molten out of a rock sixteen small stones; and they were white and clear, even as transparent glass ..." (3:1). A possible inference of glass is also recorded in Ether. Here the statement is, "What will ye that I [the Lord] should do that ye may have light in your vessels? For behold, ye cannot have windows, for they will be dashed to pieces ..." (2:23).

Now, back to the critics. They have used the existence of glass in the New World as an argument against the validity of the Book of Mormon, claiming it wasn't present in the Americas during this time. If so, then they have not read the Book carefully. As noted above, the glass (actually glasses) mentioned in the Nephite record is just a quote from Isaiah. The glass referred to in the Jaredite record was one made while these people were still somewhere in the Old World - not yet in the Americas. Some critics have said that there was no record of glass even in the Old World at the time of the Jaredites.

Therefore this, too, would cast doubts on the Book of Mormon being a true account. However, this is also a false assumption. Glass beads and other glass objects are known from ancient Egyptian and Mesopotamian archeological sites. Obtained dates for these go back over 3000 years B.C. (Diamond, 1953, p. 10: Macfarlane and Martin, 2002, p. 10). This significantly predates the Jaredite record.

Glass has actually been around in different forms before man was on earth. Volcanic glass is one type. It is not transparent, though, such as the kind listed in Ether (3:1). Another type of glass is produced when lightning strikes sand or a sandy soil. This kind of glass is known as a fulgurite. Thin pieces of fulgurite can be transparent depending upon the composition of the sand struck. However, this kind of glass is very irregular in shape, and difficult to work.

Another type of natural "glass" is isinglass. At one time it was commonly used for windows, especially in horse-drawn carriages of various types. This material is a mica called muscovite, which is usually "white and clear" as mentioned in the scripture above. If isinglass were the material considered by the brother of Jared for barge windows, these windows would have been "dashed in pieces" (Ether 2:23), if strong waves struck them. However, it just isn't known whether the Jaredites were able to produce glass or not. But since there is no record of them actually producing or having (glass) in the New World, there can be no valid criticism regarding this issue.

4

Linen and Silk in the Book of Mormon

Some critics have objected to the fact that linen, especially fine-twined linen, is mentioned in the Book of Mormon and have stated that it was not "supposed to be" in the Americas before the Spaniards came. Examples of this material in Book of Mormon times are given in Alma (1:29), and Ether (10:24). But the key question is, what qualifies as linen? When linen is mentioned today – at least in the United States – most people think of sheets and pillow cases. The majority of these are made from cotton. Hemp and other plant fibers when woven tightly enough are sometimes called linen. What is considered true linen is made of fibers from the flax plant. Fine paper is also produced from linen.

Usage shows that the term "linen" can be used both in a specific sense and a general one. So, even without a language translation involved, different interpretations of linen are possible. So-called true linen (i.e., linen made from flax fibers) is known from ancient times, even before the Jaredite history begins. Egyptian mummies are wrapped in one type of linen going back more than 3000 B.C., centuries before the start of the Jaredite history.

The question now arises, did the Jaredite and Nephite linen come from flax? The Book of Mormon tells us that each group brought seeds with them from the Old World. Other plant fibers, too, those found in the New World, could produce a cloth that might be similar enough to Old World linen to give it the same name. Flax is an Old World plant. It was much prized in ancient times as a durable fabric. Jared, his brother, and the others that came to America with them were probably aware of this material, and the plant from which it was made. Knowing the value of linen to people in the Old World, it is reasonable to assume that flax seeds would have been brought to America by the Jaredites. The same would hold true for Lehi and his family.

According to Brigham Young University professors, Terry B. Ball and Wilford M. Hess, both the Jaredites and Nephites, "...in all probability brought flax seeds with them on their trek to the promised land." (2004, p. 174). They also indicated that since flax does well without cultivation, that it might have been present by the time the Nephites arrived. And, according to Hess, flax could still be in the Americas as a result of this introduction millennia ago (2008, Pers. Comm.)

Whether the "fine-twined" linen of the Book of Mormon was manufactured from flax is unknown. However, as implied above, they could call other finely woven fabric, linen. Then as now, cotton might have been used. Cotton is native to both the Old and New Worlds, and would probably have been available to Jaredites as well as Nephites.

Silk is another item that Book of Mormon critics say was not present in America before Europeans settled here. But, like linen, there is more than one possible source. Historically, people have generally regarded silk as a fine fabric obtained from the cocoons of the mulberry silkworm larvae. However, cocoons of other kinds of caterpillar larvae are also used to make silk. The product looks the same even though the quality differs.

Silks have been produced in many different parts of the world. It should not be surprising, then, that silk is mentioned as a fabric in the Book of Mormon (e.g., Alma 4:6; Ether 10:24). In fact in the Ether account it is reported that, "And they (the Jaredites) did have silks..." The implication here is that they may have had more than one type. If so, the different types could have been produced from the cocoons of different kinds of caterpillar larvae.

Other possibilities for different types of silk exist as well. John L. Sorenson commented, "Moreover, fine hair from the belly of rabbits of central Mexico was woven into a cloth which the Spanish considered equal in finish and texture to silk." (1995, p. 10). Both Sorenson and Hess considered that fiber from the ceiba (kapok) tree of Mesoamerica has been spun to form a silk-like material (Hess, 2008, Pers. Comm.). This substance also would have been available to both the Jaredites and Nephites.

5

Food Plants in the Book of Mormon

Some different familiar grains are briefly listed in the Book of Mormon (e.g., barley, wheat, and corn), along with two unfamiliar ones, neas, and sheum. (Mosiah 9:9). Although the Jaredites brought seeds to the New World from the Old, types are not specified (Ether 1:41). It is stated, however, that they did have some types of grain (Ether 9:17; 10:12).

The presence of barley and wheat, which originally are Old World grains, caused many Book of Mormon critics to state that this alone challenges the veracity of the Book. As most people know corn (or maize) is a New World plant. The mention of "corn" in the Bible is usually understood as a general term, and includes different types of grain (e.g., Genesis 41:5; Isaiah 28:28). According to Ball and Hess, "It is generally believed that maize originated in Mexico and was domesticated from wild maize ..." (2004, p. 163).

Possibly the Nephites domesticated a variety of maize, or corn, as they seemingly lived in the southern part of Mexico to Guatemala (Sorenson, 1985, p. 37). As related in Ball and Hess, domesticated maize dates between 5000 and 3000 B.C. (2004, p. 164).

The major objection to plants "that shouldn't be" in the Book of Mormon has mostly centered on barley and wheat. Since these are Old World grains, and "would not occur" in the Americas before Columbus, the critics have made much of this. However, archaeologist Daniel B. Adams reported that barley had been recovered from a site in Arizona (1983, p. 32, 37). Archaeologists Nancy and David Asch discovered further evidence for barley in America in Oklahoma and Illinois that predates the arrival of Spaniards (1985, p. 79). Although this is a different variety of barley than that of the Old World, as might be expected, it nonetheless is still barley. Wheat yet seemingly presents a problem. To my knowledge this grain has never been identified in Precolumbian time in America.

Keep in mind that barley was not found in America until fairly recently, though, even after a century of extensive archaeological digs have taken place in North and Central America. What we do know of wheat is, that it, too, is an Old World grain. It was probably first domesticated in the upper parts of the Tigris and Euphrates Rivers in an area known as the Fertile Crescent (Lev-Yardun et al., 2000, p. 1602).

Wheat was grown anciently in many Old World civilizations. Joseph of Egypt, ancestor of Lehi (1 Nephi 5:14), was in charge of Pharaoh's extensive granaries. While the general term for grain, "corn", is used in Genesis, the main type was most likely wheat. Ancient wheat is certainly known from Egypt. One of the reasons for a lack of evidence of wheat in the Americas in Precolumbian time was explained by Ball and Hess. They stated, "The cultivated species of wheat and barley the Lehites [Nephites and Lamanites] would have had available to them were already highly domesticated by the seventh century B.C. Domesticated plants generally cannot survive without human intervention." (2004, p. 152).

Therefore, wheat could have been present at the time of the Nephites, but later became extinct as a domesticated plant after generations of neglect. Archaeologists John L. Sorenson and Carl L. Johannessen also commented on the problem of maintaining domesticated life. They said, "Domesticated plants and animals are almost never successfully transplanted by humans to a strange area without appropriate care being given the transplanted specimens." (2006, p. 277).

Concerning wheat, I think that there will probably come a time when evidence for it will be discovered in Precolumbian America by archaeologists. Its absence to date, though, should not cause anyone to question their faith as to the authenticity of the Book of Mormon.

The names "neas" and "sheum" as given in the Book of Mosiah, must be ones representing some type of edible plant. They are mentioned in conjunction with corn, wheat, and barley, so they might represent types of grains. However, this cannot be known for a surety. Why the strange names, though? It would seem that Joseph Smith did not have a knowledge of any plant with which to relate them. Apparently, he just used the original untranslated names, or else they appeared to him in that form. This might also be the case with two animals mentioned in the Jaredite record, cureloms and cumoms (Ether 9:19). These animals are discussed in a later chapter of this book.

6

Animals in the
Book of Mormon

From my first reading of the Book of Mormon I had a special interest in the animals listed in both the Jaredite and Nephite records. The animals mentioned by the two peoples were very similar, but yet not the same. My interest grew as I took biology and later paleontology classes in college. Then with my own research into Pleistocene (Ice Age) mammals, this interest grew still more. Could all the animals mentioned have been in North and Central America during the times of the Jaredites and Nephites? My studies confirmed that, yes, they all could be depending upon certain interpretations. Of course these animals included those enigmatic beasts, the cureloms and cumoms. While their identifications can only be considered guesses on my part, there are some good candidates. Again, as with these and other animals (specifically mammals useful to man), Book of Mormon critics take issue, saying most were only in the New World after the time of Columbus. Those like the horse were said to have become extinct in America long before the time of either the Jaredites or the Nephites. Well, let's see if those critics can be proven wrong.

There are two different problems in properly identifying animals in both the Jaredite and Nephite records. One is, we can't be positive that each animal with its translated name[3] exactly corresponds to our present understanding of that animal. I do think, though, that the terms used are probably close approximations. Al-

---

[3] Even using the same language, a given animal can have different names (e.g., mountain lion, cougar, puma). Also, two different animals can have the same name (e.g., the North American "moose" is known as an "elk" in Europe, while the North American "elk" is a very different animal). Therefore, care needs to be taken in the interpretation of stated animals in the Book of Mormon. It's best to allow some flexibility in thinking.

though John L. Sorenson expressed the idea that not all the animals stated in the Book of Mormon are what we might think them to be, he does think that most of them can be accounted for. His comment on this was, "Present knowledge of the species in Mesoamerica indicates there were enough of the right sorts of animals in that setting that all twelve of the Book of Mormon's beasts [listed animals] can be plausibly accounted for." (1985, p. 291).

The other problem is actually two-fold. It concerns which native American animals have historically been considered extinct before the Spaniards came to America, and those thought not to have existed in the New World before being introduced by them.

The animals listed in the Book of Ether are: cattle, oxen, cows, sheep, swine[4], goats, horses, asses, elephants, cureloms, and cumoms (9:18-19). Those listed in 1 Nephi are: cow, ox, ass, horse, goat, and wild goat (18:25). Both lists are only partial as the two records indicate that there were other animals available for the use of man. Reason would also dictate that many other animals were present in the areas that both the Jaredites and Nephites settled. An interesting thing about these animals is that all, except the wild goat, probably were semi-domesticated to domesticated, or at least tamed. Some doubt arises in the case of the cureloms and cumoms. But the scripture does state that they were especially useful to man (Ether 9:19). A possible present-day identity for these two beasts is that one definitely could have been domesticated, and the

---

[4] It surprises some people that swine are recorded in the Book of Ether as a food item (Ether 9:18). A commandment not to eat this animal wasn't given until the Lord told Moses that swine were not to be eaten by the Israelites (Leviticus 11:7). The only mention of swine in the Nephite record (3 Nephi 7:8, and 14:6) is in a negative sense. They were not for food to them.

other possibly so, or at least tamed and put to use. These animals will be discussed in more detail in Chapter 11.

The domesticated animals named in the Book of Mormon, are cattle, swine, sheep, goats, the horse, and the ass. Many scientists have considered these beasts to be either extinct or never present in America before Columbus introduced European kinds on his four voyages. While I believe that all or most of these animals could have been brought to America by Jaredites, there were comparable native American types that would have been present during both Jaredite and Nephite times. They will be discussed separately.

An interesting distinction can be made between the animal records of the Jaredites and the Nephites. In the case of the Jaredites, it's stated that they brought, "... their flocks and herds, and whatsoever beast or animal or fowl that they should carry with them -" (Ether 6:4). They also brought fish in a specially built container, as well as swarms of honey bees[5] (Ether 2:2-3). In the Nephite record it's written that many of the animals mentioned in the Jaredite record were already in the New World when they arrived. These are the cow, ox, goat, ass and horse. (1 Nephi 18:25). No mention is made of the Nephites bringing animals from the Old World with them, although they may well have done so. Only a mention of seeds being brought from the land of Jerusalem is recorded (1 Nephi 18:17).

---

[5] Honey bees originated in the Old World, probably in Southeast Asia, and were not thought to be present in the Americas before European colonization began. Obviously, since these European colonizers would have brought bees by boat, the Jaredites should have been able to do so as well. Bees can be transported over relatively long periods of time in a dormant state.

We are dealing with a complex problem in trying to explain what animals were already in the New World when the Jaredites, then Nephites, arrived. One reason is that none of those brought by the Jaredites, except the honey bee, is named. The terms "flocks" and "herds" (Ether 6:4), could allow for a variety of animals. A further complicating factor is that the English word for "flock" could apply to birds or to certain mammals like sheep and goats. The Jaredites were already in America (probably Mesoamerica) five generations before any named animals are given (Ether 9:18-19). With the paucity of information provided, we can't be sure which animals had originally been transported by Jared and his group, and which were already present in the areas where they settled. We can at least work out some possibilities, however. These need to satisfy both the scriptural and scientific records.

It seems very likely that the Jaredites would only have brought domesticated animals on the barges with them, ones they thought sure would be beneficial. Now, what sizes of animals could they bring? The mention of herds (if the translated word involved means what it does now) suggests that at least some were large. How large, or how many of each kind we don't know. I think, though, that we can be sure that enough of each kind were brought along to insure a breeding population could be established. What about the individual sizes of larger animals? It occurred to me, without knowing size limitations on the barges, that fully mature (and therefore larger) individuals were not necessary. Bringing just young and smaller individuals could be advantageous both for space and food needs. With all this in mind, I think that cattle (oxen and cows), sheep, goats, swine, asses and horses could conceivably have been brought on the voyage.

Was the bringing of larger animals probable? I don't know. But, at least it seems possible. None-the-less, native counterparts of each of these animals named above were present in America. This presents us with another problem though. Several of these kinds of animals, as well as the elephant (and possibly the curelom and cumom), were considered extinct by most paleontologists on the order of 10,000 to 12,000 years ago. This was the close of the Pleistocene (Ice Age) epoch. If they are considered to be extinct, how could they then be included in the record of the Jaredites?

As previously stated, criticisms have been leveled against the Book of Mormon because of the animals listed, such as the elephant, horse and ass. Critics have stated that these were extinct thousands of years prior to the Book of Mormon peoples being in the New World. With the information provided above, it should be fairly clear that the chances of now finding evidences of these animals at the time of the Jaredite and Nephite records are actually small. For one thing the region of concern was probably quite limited (Sorenson, 1985, p. 37). Another reason in my opinion is, only relatively small numbers of the indicated animals were present in the region. Therefore, there would be less chance for preserved remains.

Then, as now, the vast majority of their bones left after death would disintegrate upon exposure to the elements, turning to dust. Additionally, there were times when extensive famine-causing droughts came upon both the Jaredites and Nephites. Great numbers of animals would have died along with the people (Ether 9:30-34; 11:7). Although famines also took place among the Nephites and Lamanites, the effects on the animals is not noted (Alma 62:35; Helaman 11:4). Even so, these famines must have seriously reduced animal populations. Could these famines have caused any extinctions, at least locally? Possibly they might have done this. It should be indicated here that droughts do occur in semi-tropical regions, such as those postulated for at least some of the lands in which the Jaredites and Nephites lived. It has been stated that, … "Classical Maya civilization collapsed as a result of a drought in Mesoamerica extending throughout the 9th Century A.D" (Gill, 2000).

Another circumstance that would have led to a paucity of animal evidence being available to us now, relates to the climatic conditions under which they probably lived. This is a critical factor. Assuming that both Jaredites and Nephites lived in what now constitutes part of Mesoamerica, climatic conditions would have been unfavorable for preserving evidences of life. Most of this region during the time they lived there, like now, is in a tropical to subtropical belt.

When organisms die in this type of environment, they quickly decompose and disintegrate. The many mountainous areas of Mesoamerica are also not conducive to preservation. Here, shortly after death skeletons of organisms are washed away, being broken up in the process, until no recognizable parts remain. There are some exceptions to having conditions so unfavorable for the preservation of past life in this region. One is the presence of a number of caves. As indicated below, caves have provided some interesting finds. Another situation where past life can escape complete destruction, is when the hard parts of an animal are quickly buried, such as in the sediments of a lake or a flood plain. Considering all the circumstances, I'm not surprised by so little evidence being available to support the animals reported in the Book of Mormon. However, some evidences do exist. These should be sufficient to leave open the probability of more being found.

7

Cattle in the Book of Mormon

A rchaeologists as well as paleontologists have been finding more and more associations of animals, extinct as well as extant, with man at a number of sites in America. (e.g., Harrington, 1933; Irwin-Williams, 1967; Schmidt, 1988; Pichardo, 2000a, 2000b; Arroyo-Cabrales and Alvarez, 2003).

The first of the animals to be discussed are the cattle, oxen, and cows. These are listed in the Jaredite record (Ether 9:18). The cow and ox are also reported in the Nephite record (1Nephi 18:25). Whether there are any distinctions to be made between those animals in the two records is unclear. However, I assume that two different types of closely related animals are meant. Is there any evidence for domestic cattle being associated with either the Jaredite or the Nephite peoples? There may be some!

The presence of cattle as identified by bones of a domestic type *Bos taurus* (Figure 1a & 1b) has been reported by Hatt from three caves (Lara, Has, and Loltún) in the Yucatan Peninsula (1953, p. 27, 29). What makes this especially interesting is that these bones were found in association with an extinct horse. Perhaps of greater interest is that human artifacts have also been recovered from these caves that may relate to the same age. According to paleontologists Joaquin Arroyo-Cabrales and Oscar J. Polaco, the presence of this horse seems to indicate that it survived into historic time (2003, p. 283). Another cave (Gruta de Loltún) on the Yucatan Peninsula also contains the domestic cattle species, *Bos taurus* (Arroyo-Cabrales and Alvarez, 2003, p. 263).

.

Figure 1a. This Egyptian tomb painting is of Sennutem (overseer of the Royal Egyptian tombs) plowing with domestic cattle of the species *Bos taurus*. It was discovered near Thebes, Egypt, and has been dated at c.1200 B.C. The time of this Egyptian tomb painting corresponds to the same time that the Jaredites were living in the New World. The first Jaredites conceivably brought this cattle species with them. *Bos taurus* bones and teeth have been found in caves of the Yucatan Peninsula of Mexico and elsewhere along with prehistoric artifacts. *(Courtesy of Wikipedia Commons, Yorck project – Public Domain)*

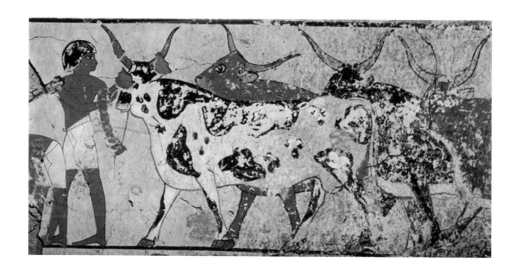

Figure 1b.   The Egyptian tomb painting shown here is from near Thebes, Egypt. It, too, depicts domesticated cattle of the species *Bos taurus*. The dating of this painting has been placed at c.1422-1411 B.C. A number of ancient petroglyphs and rock carvings indicate that Egyptians domesticated cattle by at least 4500 B.C. according to some archaeologists. These dates also correspond to the same time that the Jaredites were living in the New World. *(Courtesy of Wikipedia Commons, Yorck project – Public Domain)*

Cattle

Other caves in the region yet need exploring for vertebrate mammals in association with man. While some research has been done, it is still in initial stages. Undoubtedly more information will come forth showing that animals some viewed as extinct actually continued into historic times. As far as native American "cattle," there are at least three types which could represent the ones referred to in the Book of Mormon

One of these is the native American bison (buffalo), which is known throughout North and Central America from the latter part of the Pleistocene to fairly recent time. Its once exceptionally large geographic range, though, has been greatly reduced because of expanding civilization, beginning with European settlers. Different species of bison are known to have coexisted with man before becoming extinct. Two of these are illustrated in Figure 2. Sorenson reported that early Spaniards regarded bison as "cows" (1992, p. 12). From personal observations in different regions, I have seen that the bison (or buffalo) can be semi-domesticated. Possibly this was one of the animals referred to as "cow" in the Book of Mormon. It might also be regarded as an "ox." Another candidate for a cattle-type animal perhaps known to Book of Mormon people is the extinct shrub-ox.

While supposedly extinct at the close of the Pleistocene, it might have well survived into historic times. I have examined a skull of this ox-like animal from southern Mexico (Carranza-Castañeda and Miller, 1987, P. 339-340). One final ox-type mammal in North America is the extinct woodland muskox (Figure 3). It, too, could easily have lived into historic times. Both the shrub-ox and woodland muskox are considered to be animals that lived primarily in wooded areas. Those that live in this type of an environment do not commonly get preserved as fossils. Both kinds of native ox, are considered relatively rare.

Figure 2. Represented here are two species of extinct bison known until the latest Pleistocene, and quite possibly later. Both species are larger than our present bison. The giant bison, *Bison latifrons,* is on the left, and the smaller bison, *Bison antiquus,* is on the right. *Bison,* especially the smaller living species, *B. bison,* could well be included among some of the cattle mentioned in the Book of Mormon. *(Figure by courtesy of the George C. Page Museum in southern California. John Dawson, artist. From Harris and Jefferson, 1985, "Treasures of the Tar Pits.")*

From the above information it can be seen that the cattle mentioned in the Book of Mormon, both in the Jaredite and Nephite records, could be accounted for by the native oxen that were present in Mesoamerica as well as in North America. It does not take a great stretch of the imagination to believe that both the shrub-ox and woodland muskox were capable of being at least semi-domesticated. Man has in fact semi-domesticated the living northern muskox.

Figure 3. Restoration of extinct woodland muskoxen, *Bootherium bombifrons*, with a native hunter looking for bison. Muskoxen, recent and extinct forms, are also a type of cattle, and the extinct form here could have been encountered by the Jaredites. Living muskoxen, however, are now confined to Arctic regions, and commonly used for food and clothing by Alaskan Inuit people. *(From Miller, 2002, "Quaternary Vertebrates of the Northeastern Bonneville Basin and Vicinity, Utah." Original painting in the Prehistoric Museum, Price, Utah. Joe Venus, artist)*

8

Swine in the
Book of Mormon

Swine were designated as another kind of animal used for food by Jaredites (Ether 9:18). It was not stated, however, if these animals were among the ones brought over on the barges by them. As I see it, there are two alternative possibilities regarding their presence in North America. True swine, or pigs, as we understand the terms now, relate to an Old World animal. They were never native to the New World as evidence from fossils and DNA studies show. Thus, if this specific animal is the type meant in the Book of Ether, it had to be imported. To my knowledge there have not been Precolumbian archaeological finds where Old World pigs were found associated with man. But even in the absence of such evidence, it is possible they were in the New World in limited numbers, in a restricted area, and then became extinct when no longer domestically raised. There is another possibility for inclusion of swine in the Jaredite record.

The peccary (or javelina) (Figure 4) is a New World animal that essentially parallels and is closely related to the Old World pigs. There are several extinct forms as well as three living kinds. These, too, are commonly referred to as pigs, and have been used for a food item for several thousand years. In fact they are still used for food throughout their range. Peccaries have been found associated with human artifacts in the Loltún Cave in the Yucatán Peninsula as reported by Arroyo-Cabrales and Alvarez (2003, p. 264-266). These animals were earlier reported in this general region by Hatt from several caves (Lara, Coyok, Spukil, and Chacaljas), which were commonly associated with human artifacts (1953, p. 30-36).

Figure 4. Restoration of the extinct peccary, *Platygonus compressus*, known from many fossil localities in North America, including Mexico. Its size was equal to the European wild boar. Peccaries, both living and extinct forms, are commonly referred to as pigs. They easily could represent the swine referred to in the Book of Ether. Of course the Jaredites could have brought swine from the Old World with them. These animals are not mentioned in the Nephite record as a food item as the Nephites observed the Law of Moses. *(Figure by courtesy of the George C. Page Museum in southern California. John Dawson, artist. From Harris and Jefferson, 1985, "Treasures of the Tar Pits.")*

Two living types of peccary still inhabit Mesoamerica. It was thought that one species from South America was extinct; however, it was later found to still be living (Kurtén and Anderson, 1980, p. 296). One type of extinct peccary from Florida survived until at least 7,000 to 8,000 years ago, and possibly to 5,000 years ago (Martin and Webb, 1974, p. 144).

Although I am not aware of any Precolumbian true, or Old World, pigs discovered in the New World, it has to be considered a possibility that they were in America. They are definitely known from very early historic times. Being in limited numbers in a restricted region, their evidence might have escaped detection to date. As more field studies take place, more and more types of life that were "not supposed to be in America" have been discovered. This holds true for fossils and, as reported by Sorenson and Johannessen, certain domesticated plants and animals (2006, p. 238).

9

Sheep and Goats in the Book of Mormon

As mentioned earlier, sheep and goats were listed in conjunction with Book of Mormon peoples, both Jaredites and Nephites. Neither of their records, though, specifically states whether these types of animals were brought over from the Old World. However, it does seem reasonable that they were, as both sheep and goats were valuable resources to man there. They seemingly would have been included in the "flocks and herds" cited in Ether (6:4). In the Jaredite record we are told that they, "were useful for the food of man." (Ether 9:18).

Then, as now, the wool from sheep could also be used to make clothing. Sorenson relayed that sheep's wool was found at a Precolumbian burial site near Puebla, Mexico (1985, p. 296-297). Assuming both sheep and goats were brought over by the Jaredites (and perhaps by Lehi and his group), is it possible that closely related types of animals were also already in Mesoamerica when they arrived?

The statement that there were both goats and wild goats that the Nephites found in the forests upon arrival in the Promised Land (1 Nephi 18:25), suggests to me that the non-wild goats encountered were a former domesticated breed. Possibly this was an Old World species that the Jaredites had earlier brought over with them. The early Nephites would have seen a difference between Old World goats with which they were familiar, and a new type unseen by them before.

There is only one living species of wild goat in North America (Figure 5). Its current geographic range, from Alaska south to the northwestern United States, would seem to keep it from consideration as the "wild goat" mentioned in 1 Nephi (18:25). However, a closely related species is known as a late Pleistocene fossil that had a more southerly distribution. In fact it is known from Mesoamerica. Fossils of this animal are known mostly from cave deposits.

Figure 5. This photo of the living mountain goat provides a general idea of what the extinct species, *Oreamnos harringtoni*, looked like. However, the extinct form with a range into Mexico was somewhat smaller, with longer and more curved horns. This wild goat is possibly depicted in the petroglyphs shown in Figure 6 below. Both the Jaredite and Nephite records indicate the presence of goats. Wild goats are also given in the Nephite record. *Oreamnos harringtoni* is probably the wild goat that they encountered. (*Photo by courtesy of the U.S. Fish and Wildlife Service*)

As mentioned before, several Late Pleistocene animals survived into historic times. This goat could easily be one of these. Their fossils, though, are very rare. According to Kurtén and Anderson, "mountain goats are rare as fossils partly because their habitat is not conducive to fossil preservation." (1980, p. 372).

Fossils of mountain goat have been found in San Josecito Cave in northern Mexico (Arroyo-Cabrales and Johnson, 1995, p. 223). Bones of Precolumbian domestic goat were reported from caves in the Yucatan Peninsula of Mexico (Hatt, 1953, p. 29). Both the wild goat and the domestic goat could have been encountered by the Nephites as reported. It's possible, if not probable, that the only sheep listed by the Jaredites and Nephites were a domestic breed. Only two kinds of sheep are known from the Pleistocene as well as the Recent (= Post-Pleistocene or Ice Age) from North America.

One, the Dall sheep, is only found native in Alaska, the Yukon, the Northwest Territories and northern British Columbia. It would not be a good candidate for a type of sheep in Book of Mormon lands. If the sheep mentioned in the Book of Mormon was a native variety, it would be the Bighorn sheep. This animal presently has a geographic range from southwestern Canada to northern Mexico.

Before European settlement of the New World, this sheep had a more extensive range, which included foothills and meadows as well as mountains. It has been stated that, "... with the advent of white man, they [Bighorn sheep] moved into the mountains and are now found only in mountainous areas." (Hall and Kelson, 1959, p. 1031). Before this time, when they could more readily be preserved as fossils, they left a modest record of their presence, at least in some areas. Gypsum Cave in southern Nevada has yielded fossils of Bighorn sheep along with several types of extinct animals. Some of the bones found here show signs of charring, as well as cut marks attributed to man (Glowiak and Rowland, 2003, p. 498). Many human artifacts have also been collected in Gypsum Cave (Harrington, 1933). There are a number of localities in the American Southwest, many of which I've visited, that show petroglyphs of sheep – and possibly goats - some with human figures alongside them (Figure 6).

Figure 6. A photograph of petroglyphs from Newspaper Rock in southwestern Utah. Sheep and possibly goats are shown among the animals depicted. It appears that utilizing these animals was a practice of ancient peoples in the New World. This would certainly apply to both the Jaredites and the Nephites as well. The petroglyphs shown here date back many centuries according to archaeologists. *(Photo by author)*

Certainly the association of sheep and goats with man before European settlement of America is established. As previously stated, translated words might not carry the same meaning as we place on them today. Therefore, what we call sheep (or another animal in the Book of Mormon) could possibly represent something different. For example, when the Spaniards came to the Americas, they commonly called the llama-like animals, guanacos and vicuñas, "native sheep."

10

Elephants in
the Book of Mormon

When I first read the Book of Ether in the Book of Mormon, I was *very* surprised to see that elephants were listed as one of the animals the Jaredites found in America. The question that ran through my mind was: "Is that possible?" It must have been that I took it on faith that it was, as I believed the Book of Mormon to be true from my first reading of it. Even so, my mind was put more at ease a few years later when I took a geology class and saw how this could be. Little did I realize then that some years later I'd be collecting many fossils of this magnificent beast, and doing research on them.

There is only a name change that should help people get over the hurdle of elephants appearing in the Book of Mormon as native to the New World. We now know these elephants as mammoths. Originally they came to this continent from Eurasia during the Pleistocene. For many years paleontologists called mammoths, elephants, as they wrote about them.[6] Some still do. The Columbian mammoth of North America, based on studies of its fossils, is more closely related to the Indian (or Asian) elephant than the Indian elephant is to the African one! Often when people hear of a mammoth, the Woolly mammoth comes to their minds. That's the one I used to think of first. However, even though this kind might be the most famous, it apparently was not nearly as abundant as the Columbian mammoth. Both, though, are elephants.

---

[6] Examples of what are now called mammoths, earlier being referred to as elephants, can be found in the following articles or books: Arellano, 1951; Furlong, 1925; Johnson, 1952; Kalb and Mebrate, 1993; Osborn, 1942. For a complete reference of these citations see the References Cited at the back of this book.

With its long shaggy hair and thick wool undercoat, the Woolly mammoth was especially well adapted to live in cold climates. Its geographic range spread over the northern parts of the North American and Eurasia continents. Even in North America it's highly unlikely that any Book of Mormon people lived where these mammoths ranged.

If the "elephant"[7] recorded in the Book of Ether (9:19) really was the animal I envision, it would have been the Columbian mammoth. This animal is well represented by fossils throughout North America in the late Pleistocene. In the research I have done in Mexico, it is the most numerous of late Pleistocene fossils in some areas. It's stated in the passage in Ether above, that the elephant was especially useful to man. Although it is not mentioned as a food item (as are cattle, sheep, goats, and swine in verse18), there is a good chance that it was utilized as such. Sites where man and mammoth are associated in North America are not uncommon. A statement was made that, "There can no longer be any reasonable doubt that man and elephant coexisted in America." (Johnson, 1952, p. 216).

Many more joint occurrences have been reported since this statement was made. At a number of such sites, spear points have been found associated with the fossils, and in some instances still embedded in bone (Martin, 2005, p. 148-149). Mammoth kill sites are known at several localities in Mesoamerica (e.g., Johnson, 1952, p. 216; MacNeish and Nelken-Terner, 1983, p. 73, 76; Pich-

---

[7] There were two other elephant-like animals that lived in North and Central America after the Pleistocene. One was the American mastodon, and the other a distant relative called a gomphothere. Both have been found in association with man in Mesoamerica.

49

ardo, 2001, p. 42). I have seen petroglyphs that appear to depict the American mastodon and possibly the mammoth in Utah. One is seen in Figure 7.

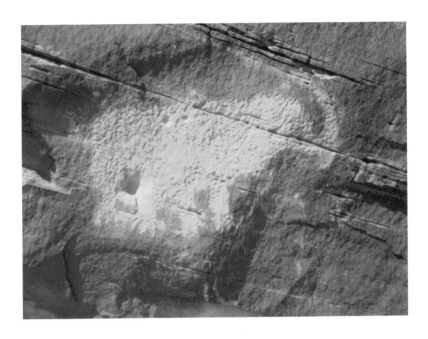

Figure 7. Petroglyph of a probable mastodon (its shape is much closer to a mastodon than a mammoth) from near Moab, Utah. Both mammoth and mastodon fossils have been found–associated with prehistoric man in North America. Each of these animals could have been encountered by Jaredite peoples. This figure is etched in sandstone, and is roughly 20 inches long. The holes seen both within and above the figure were made by gun shots. *(Photo by author)*

As far as elephants being useful to man (Ether 9:19), that is certainly easy to accept. Even today elephants are used as beasts of burden. They are ridden as well. These practices have gone back several thousand years in Asia and the Middle East. Domestication of the Indian elephant, as based on evidence found in the Indus Valley, goes back at least to 2500 B.C. (Bist et al., 2001).

Elephants at present have primarily been used to lift and move heavy loads, such as logging in southeast Asian forests. In the past they were used even in ancient warfare (Keegan, 1993, p. 271). The type of elephant most used by man has been with the Indian elephant. African elephants have proved to be much more difficult to train. Indian elephants on the other hand can be semi-domesticated. Circus elephants are this type. With the realization that the Columbian mammoth (Figure 8) is very closely related to the Indian elephant, it should not be a surprise that Jaredites could use this animal to do work.

Before coming to America Jared and his companions possibly saw the elephant being used as a beast of burden. This is especially likely if their route to the ocean was through Asia as Hugh Nibley thought (1988, p. 181-182). If this were true, Jared and his group would have learned that elephants could be of great use. This agrees with what we are told in Ether 9:19 – that elephants were especially useful to man.

There is overwhelming evidence that man and mammoth were associated in America for a fairly extensive period of time. That elephants (mammoths) are listed as an animal known to the Jaredites, but apparently not to the Nephites, suggests that their extinction probably occurred between these times. No unequivocal dating of the mammoth puts them close to the time Nephites were in America.

Figure 8. The Columbian mammoth (actually a true elephant) shown here was a common animal from Alaska through Central America in the Pleistocene epoch. It apparently survived beyond this time. Some individuals were larger than any known modern elephant. Like the modern elephant they would have been useful to man. It is indicated in the Book of Ether that the elephant was one of the animals that was especially useful for the Jaredites. *(Figure by courtesy of the George C. Page Museum in southern California. John Dawson, artist. From Harris and Jefferson, 1985, "Treasures of the Tar Pits.")*

Until the last few decades, almost all scientists were convinced that mammoths did not survive the Pleistocene (Ice Age) epoch. This was 10,000 to 12,000 years ago (Agenbroad, 1984, p. 99). However, more and more datings on these fossils show that they lived on much longer. How long did they survive?

That question is still being debated by paleontologists. Mario Pichardo listed a last appearance date for the North American mammoth at 8,260 years ago (2001, p. 44). James Mead and David Meltzer claimed a younger date of 4,885 years ago (1984, p. 446). Recently David Yesner, Douglas Veltre, Kristine Crossen, and Russell Graham reported an age for an Alaskan mammoth of 5,720 years (2005, p. 202). S. L.Vartanyan, V. E. Garutt, and A. V. Sher dated mammoth fossils from Wrangel Island near Alaska at 3,700 years ago (1993, p. 340). An exceptionally young age was given for a site in St. Petersburg, Florida, where mammoth fossils were found. According to James Hester, this animal lived on until 2,040 years ago (1960, p. 72) It should be acknowledged, however, that most scientists do not accept this date as valid (Martin, 2005, p. 122).

What should be realized with the facts given above, is that scientific evidence does give credence to the Book of Mormon claim that elephants (mammoths) were present in America when the Jaredites first settled.

11

Cureloms and Cumoms

When reading the names of animals called "cureloms" and "cumoms" in the Book of Ether, most people's curiosity is immediately piqued. What could these strange animals be? Well, they might not be strange at all. Any identification of them on my part has to be speculative. But it is speculation based on likely candidates. Since cureloms and cumoms are unknown to us today as actual animals by those names, my potential identifications given below could apply to either one.

First, though, why did Joseph Smith not assign recognizable animals in his translation? That is a fair question. A good possibility, which has been expressed by others, is that Joseph was not aware of any present-day animals to which he could assign them. These animals were outside his realm of experience. Probably they were extinct animals. I've wondered if relatives and friends directly asked him what these animals were? My guess is, yes.

What would have been his answer? Probably it was, "I don't know." In getting back to the translation problem, I see different possibilities. One of these is that the prophet Mormon, who abridged the record that Joseph translated, knew what these animals were, but Joseph did not. Another possibility is that Mosiah, son of king Benjamin, who translated the Jaredite record from the plates of gold (Mosiah 28:11), did not know these animals either, and simply used the Jaredite terms for them.

LDS archaeologist, John L. Sorenson, wrote that in his opinion cureloms and cumoms were large animals (1992, p. 41). This seems reasonable. They are grouped with the elephant, and separated from the other listed animals (Ether 9:18-19). Also, along with the elephant, they were written as being especially useful to man. It seems like they would qualify as beasts of burden. What are the possibilities of the identities of the curelom and cumom? Let's consider some of the candidates. While I indicated that these were probably extinct animals, perhaps they were not.

What are the possibilities of large, useful present-day beasts? Actually there are not too many to draw upon. One is the tapir (Figure 9), a relative of both the horse and rhinoceros. This animal currently lives in southern Mexico on into South America (with one species living in southeast Asia). The living tapir is bulky, with larger individuals weighing well over 600 pounds, and standing a little over three feet high (Walker et al., 1968, p. 1347). They can be tamed if caught young, but apparently have not been put to use by man.

Figure 9. This restoration is of an extinct late Pleistocene tapir, *Tapirus* sp., with its young. Extinct tapirs are known in several parts of the world, with fossils in the New World coming from North, Central, and South America. Living species are found in Central and South America, as well as Southeast Asia. All living types come from humid areas, and are semi-aquatic. *(From Harris and Jefferson, 1985, Treasures of the Tar Pits: Courtesy of the George C. Page Museum. John Dawson, artist.)*

Figure 10. Only one type of antilocaprid (or pronghorn) now survives. Several species, though, lived in the Pleistocene of North America, down through Mexico. Shown restored here is one of these extinct species, *Capromeryx minor*. The living antilocaprid represents one of the largest types, while the one depicted here is much smaller. The size range of these animals is close to that of modern deer. It nowhere states how large cureloms or cumoms were in the Book of Ether, just that these animals were especially useful to man. The antilocaprid, based on the living species, has not been domesticated but is used for food. *(Figure by courtesy of the George C. Page Museum in southern California. John Dawson, artist. From Harris and Jefferson, 1985, "Treasures of the Tar Pits.")*

Different species of deer live in Mesoamerica. However, they seem unlikely candidates to me for a curelom or cumom as all are of small size. While they can be tamed, domestication would have been (and is now) difficult. Even much larger deer relatives that live to the north, like the elk and moose, would not likely be domesticated. One other mammal to be considered is the pronghorn (commonly miscalled an antelope). This animal is native to North America and now ranges from Canada to Mexico. But it, too, is only of medium size, and not known to be domesticated (Figure 10).

There are a number of strange animals that once lived in North, Central, and South America called edentates (or xenarthrans). The armadillo is a relatively small living representative of this group as are the larger anteaters as well as the tree sloths of Central and South America. Many extinct edentates reached exceptionally large size, including the armored glyptodonts and giant ground sloths. One of these ground sloths was over 18 feet in length, and weighed an estimated three tons! A somewhat smaller form had a length of about 11 feet, and weighed approximately 3,500 pounds. (Figure 11) Four different genera are known from Mesoamerica. So, all lived in the presumed "right area." It's possible that at least some lived after the time of the late Pleistocene extinctions. At some widespread localities ground sloth hair and dung have been collected and analyzed. In fact I've examined some of this type of material from caves in Utah and Nevada. Now the problem in seriously considering any of these animals as qualifying as cureloms or cumoms, is that I don't see how they could be very useful (although armadillos are sometimes eaten by man).

Based on foot structure, they walked on the sides to back of their "hands" and feet. Additionally, they would have been among the least intelligent of contemporary mammals and it is doubtful that they could have been trained for useful tasks. The relatively small size of their brain cavities reveals this. So, now what's left?

Figure 11. This restoration shows one type of giant ground sloth, *Glossotherium harlani.* **There were several others known from the Pleistocene epoch, and possibly later, from North America. Whether this animal or its close relatives would have been useful to man, as were cureloms or cumoms mentioned in the Book of Ether, is very doubtful. The size of their brains indicates an animal that was probably not intelligent enough to be used as a beast of burden. Based on living tree sloths, their meat was probably inedible.** *(Figure by courtesy of the George C. Page Museum in southern California. John Dawson, artist. From Harris and Jefferson, 1985, "Treasures of the Tar Pits.")*

My pick for either the curelom or cumom is a member of the camel family. We know that camels have been very useful to man for millennia. But camels must have been known to Joseph Smith, so why didn't he use that name? While he must have known what a camel is, there are several related forms with which he would not be familiar, ones which look significantly different.

It is doubtful that back in 1829 when the Book of Mormon was translated, and Joseph Smith was only 23 years old (and having had very little formal education and time to study), that he knew about llamas. While they are a type of living South American camel, most people in the United States would also not have known about them at that time. Because of this, even if Mosiah translated the original Jaredite word based on his knowledge of the animal, Joseph Smith would not have known what the animal was. Now, would a llama, either an existing or a recently extinct type, have been especially useful to the Jaredites as stated in the Book of Ether (9:19)? I think so.

The following is a quote concerning the importance of the llama to man today as well as in ancient times:

"It is easy to realize the importance of the llama to the Indian, as he utilizes it almost 100 per cent, from its smallest hairs to its most insignificant droppings. Jerked llama meat nourishes the Indian; its woven fleece keeps him warm; its hide is made into the crude sandals with which he is shod; its tallow is used in making candles; braided, the long hairs serve him as rope; and the excrement, dried, constitutes a fuel which helps him ward off the penetrating chill of his treeless high altitude home." (Walker et al., 1968, p. 1377).

More than this, the llama is and has been an excellent beast of burden. They can carry heavy loads. The larger extinct types of llamas stood from six to seven feet high at the shoulder, and could have carried heavier loads than living types. Modern llamas and alpacas are both known now as domestic animals (they basically are no longer in the wild).

Living wild types like the guanaco and vicuña can be domesticated. According to archaeologists, the Old World camels have been domesticated for millennia. It is assumed that this propensity for domestication might also apply to the recently extinct members of the camel family as well. Anthropologist Ricardo Latcham stated that New World cameloids (llamas and related forms were domesticated in Precolumbian times (1922, p. 7-8). Archaeologist Jane Wheeler, in a study of llama history, indicated that the domestication of the llama goes back about 5,500 years (2003, p. 1).

The past geographic distribution of the llama, which includes many genera and species, covers most of North, Central, and South America. In the Pleistocene this group ranged from Alaska to the southern part of Argentina. As recorded by paleontologist S. David Webb, "... one of the early llama groups spread to South America, there radiated extensively, and then, in part, spread back to North America." (1974, p. 170). Several llama species were present in the Pleistocene of Mesoamerica, the presumable home of Book of Mormon peoples (Figure 12).

A few extinct species have been identified in this region. When did they actually become extinct? As reported above, many large mammals thought to have become extinct at least 10,000 years ago, have been found to have lived on much longer. One called the American camel (actually this camel is more closely related to the llama than to the Old World camel) is known as a fossil throughout North America. One young appearing specimen was found in a lava tube (cave-like cavity) in Utah.

Figure 12. Two different extinct llamas are depicted here. *Camelops* **(looking more like a camel in this depiction) is shown on the left, and** *Hemiauchenia* **on the right. They were very numerous as indicated by their fossils in North America throughout the Pleistocene - and probably later in time. Like living llamas and their relatives, they probably could have been domesticated. Living species have been domesticated for a few thousand years. They have been used by native peoples of South America for beasts of burden, food and clothing, as well as for a variety of other uses. They could easily fit the category of curelom or cumom as mentioned in the Book of Ether.** *(Figures by courtesy of the George C. Page Museum in southern California. John Dawson, artist. From Harris and Jefferson, 1985, "Treasures of the Tar Pits.")*

The special interest of this fossil is that it has dried muscle fibers attached to bone. It was also said to still retain an oily residue in the bone (Romer, 1929, p. 261-262). To my knowledge this fossil has not yet been Carbon-14 dated. This particular animal must have survived the Late Pleistocene extinction, and probably lived at a time when man was in America. A number of archaeological sites, including those in Mesoamerica, have included llama (broad sense) bones and teeth. Some of these co-occurrences in Mesoamerica have been reported in scientific literature (e.g., Irwin-Williams, 1967; Schmidt, 1988; Arroyo-Cabrales and Polaco, 2003).

Some of the more recent dates for the extinction of fossil llamas in North and Mesoamerica show that they would have been associated with man (Figure 13). A few of the recorded dates are: 8,240; 8,527; and possibly to 3,000 years ago (Mead and Meltzer, 1984, p. 441, 446); 7,400 to 8,200 years ago (Hester, 1960, p. 68, 73); 7,432 years ago (Frison et al., 1978, p. 386); ~ 3,800 years ago (Arroyo-Cabrales and Alvarez, 2003, p.265). Again it needs to be emphasized that the last recorded date for an extinct animal (such as some types of llama) does not mean it vanished from the earth at that point. Undoubtedly some small populations existed for at least hundreds, and possibly a few thousands, of years later. All things considered, I believe that some type of llama makes a good candidate for either a curelom or cumom.

We are now left to identify the other animal that could qualify as the curelom or cumom. What beasts are left from which to choose? They need to be ones that lived at the right time and in the right place - that is the time and place where the Jaredites were. Remember, too, they had to be especially useful to man. I can think of only one other general type to fit these conditions.

Figure 13. Photograph of petroglyphs on Newspaper Rock in southeastern Utah. These include what could be a llama (shown in extreme lower left corner of the picture). If this is an image of a llama, it does show that this animal was known to ancient American peoples in this region. It has been used as a beast of burden in the New World for thousands of years. This animal could easily have been known to the Jaredites. According to Bureau of Land Management archaeologists (on the information sign at the site), these petroglyphs were made over a period of many centuries. *(Photo courtesy of Robert Moore)*

This one type is represented by two different species. While these species look fairly similar, they have long separate histories as shown by their fossils. Both are now extinct. Each, though, belongs to a group (called an "Order" in biological terms) known as the Proboscidea - animals with a trunk (Figure 14). As you have guessed by now, this is the group which includes the elephants.

Of the two candidates for a curelom or cumom, the less well known is a type of gomphothere named *Cuvieronius* (scientifically named after the famous French naturalist, Georges Cuvier, 1769-1832). Based on its elephantine size, its trunk (the presence of which was determined from the character of its skull), and large tusks, it should have been about equal to an elephant in its ability to do work for man if tamed. The size of its braincase indicates that it was an intelligent animal. While a somewhat lesser candidate for a curelom or cumom in my opinion, fossil finds of *Cuvieronius* have been significant over the past three or four decades. I think that this is a lesser candidate, because my best guess is for another animal that is much more abundant, whose fossils have been found associated with man at numerous localities throughout North and Central America. *Cuvieronius* (Figure 15) had a geographic range from the southern United States, through Mesoamerica, to southern South America. (García-Bárcena, 1989, p. 47-48). A number of different localities from Mexico to Costa Rica have produced fossils of this proboscidean (Lucas and Gonzalez-Leon, 1997, p. 12; Montellano-Ballesteros, 2002, p. 580). Its presence in Mexico mostly comes from fossils collected in the central and southern part of the country.

There have been some reports of *Cuvieronius* being associated with man, but they are not numerous (García-Bárcena, 1989, p. 55; Prado et al., 2001, p. 338). I could find very little information concerning when this animal became extinct. However, it is supposed that small populations might have existed until at least a few thousand years ago. Joseph Smith could not have known about this animal as it was not formally recognized or named until the early 1900's.

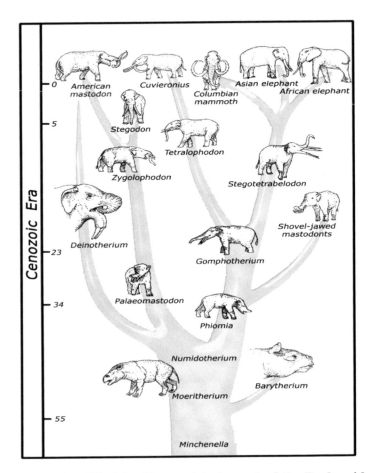

Figure 14. Simplified family tree (phylogeny) of the Proboscidea beginning with the earliest known ancestors. While there are many species that belong to this group (Order), only some of the better known types are represented here. The Columbian mammoth is evidently the elephant to which reference is made in the Book of Ether. The American mastodon and *Cuvieronius* might be either the curelom or cumom mentioned in the same book. Along with the mammoth (elephant), they both lived in the southern part of the North American continent, and presumably up until the time that the Jaredites inhabited the land. All would have been excellent beasts of burden. (*Adapted from Prothero and Dott, 2002, "Evolution of the Earth"*) [*Numbers shown on chart represent millions of years.*]

Figure 15. Restoration of the genus *Cuvieronius*, an elephant-like animal called a gomphothere (see chart on phylogeny of the Proboscidea), that lived into historic time. It ranged from the southern United States through South America. Like the American mastodon, this animal could possibly be an animal referred to as a curelom or cumom in the Book of Ether. *(Figure by courtesy of the Florida Department of Environmental Protection, Florida Geological Survey)*

The last animal to be discussed in this section as a possible curelom or cumom is the American mastodon (Figure 16). Although some mastodon fossils were known during the time of Joseph Smith, they were not well understood. In fact its fossils known at that time were considered to be of an elephant. Not until after the death of Joseph Smith were mastodon fossils in America critically studied, and a scientific name assigned (*Mammut americanum*). There is much more evidence for *Mammut* in North and Central America than for *Cuvieronius* (a gomphothere).

According to paleontologists Bjorn Kurtén and Elaine Anderson, "The American mastodon is one of the best-known Pleistocene mammals, and its remains have been found throughout the country." (1980, p. 344). Based on its fossils, the American mastodon was on average just a little shorter than the Indian elephant. However, it was of stockier build. This animal was certainly capable of being useful to man, just as the elephant is now. Its appearance, though, would have been enough different from an elephant to cause the Jaredites to call it by a separate name.

Fossils of the American mastodon are known from Alaska to Honduras, with many being discovered in Mesoamerica. To date it has never been identified in South America. This animal could apparently live in a variety of environments (which would be an advantage to man), but seemed to prefer open wooded to forested areas. While many mastodons lived in lowlands, others lived in elevations up to 10,000 feet (Miller, 1987, p. 180-181). There is no question about the mastodon being associated with man in America (e.g., Mead et al., 1979; Graham et al., 1981; Shipman et al., 1984; Fisher, 1984; García-Bárcena, 1989; Pichardo, 2001).

Considering the later recorded dates for the presence of the American mastodon, and that it would have lived for sometime after these dates, they were most likely living animals known to the Jaredites. However, mastodons seemingly became extinct before the Nephites arrived in America - at least in Book of Mormon lands. Some of the recorded later dates for living mastodons in years before the present are: 8,260 (Pichardo, 2001); 8,000 (Polaco et al., 2001); 7,590; 7,090 (Miller, 1987); 8,910; 5,950 Mead and Meltzer, 1984): 7,070; 6,300; 6,100; 5,300 (Hester, 1960).

Figure 16. American mastodon (*Mammut americanum*) is represented here in a subtropical setting. Fossils of these animals are known throughout North America, from sea level to an altitude of 10,000 feet. They were numerous in many areas and across many environments. This is an animal that could possibly be one of those referred to as a curelom or cumom in the Book of Ether. *(Restoration is by artist Heinrich Harder, 1858 - 1935).*

Another interesting aspect related to the co-existence of man and mastodon is indicated by petroglyphs. Although specific ages are not known for these, they do demonstrate they lived at the same time and in the same areas. Ones with which I have a personal knowledge are in Utah. Geologist William Lee Stokes published a brief description of them (1972, p. 84-85). In speaking with him on the matter, we both agree that the three figures represented in different locations are of a mastodon and not a mammoth.

The American mastodon is a strong possibility for being either a curelom or cumom as mentioned in the Book of Mormon. This conclusion is based on several evidences. It was certainly a large enough animal to be a very useful beast of burden. Indications based on a study of the skull of this animal are that it was intelligent, capable of being trained. Its ability to adapt to different environments makes it desirable for use. The mastodon occupied regions that must have included land inhabited by Jaredites. And there is no question that this animal lived alongside man in ancient times. Unfortunately the Jaredite record keepers did not include drawings of cureloms and cumoms.

12

Horses and Asses in the Book of Mormon

The statement in Ether 9:19 "And they also had horses, and asses ..." has caused a good deal of discussion. From what little that was recorded about animals in the Book of Ether, there is insufficient information to determine which types were brought over in "barges" to America, and which were already here when the Jaredites arrived. Obviously some were taken over by them as it's stated that they took "... food for their flocks and herds, and whatsoever beast [mammal] or animal or fowl that they should carry with them –" (Ether 6:4). The Nephites, though, found horses and asses (as well as other animals) already in the promised land upon their arrival (1 Nephi 18:25).

Even if the Jaredites did not bring these very closely related animals with them (the horse and ass), their presence can readily be explained. In the following discussion the horse and ass will be treated as one entity most of the time as they are two species belonging to the same genus, *Equus*.[8] It might be well here, though, to give some clarification relating to these two animals. An ass is also commonly called a donkey or burro.

Technically the ass is a larger animal than the donkey or burro. I rode on one while doing some field work in Mexico, being somewhat surprised at how big an animal it is. I'd ridden on horses (not ponies) that were no larger. Both the horse and ass existed as native animals in North America long before man came upon the scene. Of course all forms living here now have long since been

---

[8] Some of the fossils of smaller Pleistocene horses and asses are very difficult to distinguish from each other, especially if there are no teeth present.

domesticated. In other parts of the world the genus *Equus* is present as various kinds of zebras, as the Asian wild horse, and as varieties of the domestic horse. The mule is a hybrid animal, the result of crossing a male ass with a female horse. The mule's large size results from the large size of both the ass and the horse.

I think that more than any other animal mentioned in the Book of Mormon, the horse has generated the most debate. Critics have argued from its first printing up to the present time, that the Book of Mormon cannot be true because it states horses were in America prior to the time of Columbus. Spaniards reintroduced horses to America starting with Columbus' second voyage in 1493.

The term "reintroduced" is used, because horse fossils in America clearly show that they were here many millions of years before they were brought over by Columbus! According to paleontologist Bruce J. MacFadden, an expert on fossil horses, "Horses existed continuously in North America for about 58 million years ..." (1992, p. 304). This animal has changed dramatically, though, from the earliest forms to the present-day horse (Figure 17).

One of the best fossil records of any animal, especially in North America, is that of the horse. It is actually much better represented by its fossils than either the mastodon or mammoth. Native horses occurred in the New World from Alaska to the tip of South America. I have personally collected hundreds of their fossils, and from different ages. Most of these came from the southwestern United States and from Mexico.

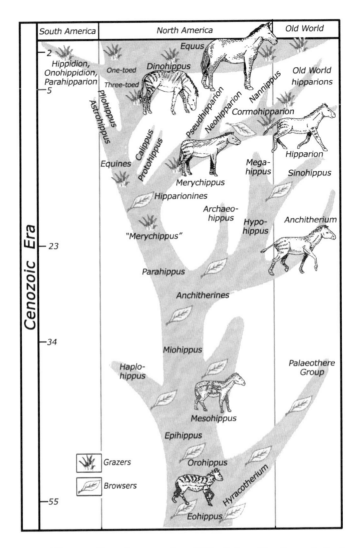

Figure 17. Chart showing a simplified family tree (phylogeny) of the horse, which had its origins in North America approximately 58 million years ago with the genus *Eohippus*. The modern genus of horse, *Equus*, has been known from fossils since before the Pleistocene epoch. It was extremely numerous throughout all North America until the end of that epoch. Obviously this was a useful beast for both Jaredites and Nephites. (*Adapted from Prothero and Dott, 2002, "Evolution of the Earth."*)

74

One of the most exciting discoveries I have had, which was in conjunction with Mexican colleagues, was in finding horse fossils that are transitional between the modern genus, *Equus*, and its immediate ancestor, *Dinohippus* (Miller and Carranza-Castañeda, 2001, p. 240). Even after careful study we could not be sure into which genus we should place some of our specimens. More fossils of this horse will be needed to help in a determination. This means that the modern horse apparently had its origin in Mexico. From there it spread to other parts of the world where it exists today in various forms - both wild and domestic.

During the Pleistocene epoch there were many species of horses and a few of asses. It is accepted by all paleontologists that these animals existed in North America until the end of this time, 10,000 to 12,000 years ago (Figure 18). Along with other Ice Age mammals listed above, evidences demonstrate that both the horse and ass survived for an appreciable time later. Some paleontologists are reluctant to accept this, though.

It's hard to change old ideas once they become ingrained. However, more and more paleontologists, as well as archaeologists, do accept some younger ages for the last native horses in America. A number of Carbon-14 dates on horse fossils, especially in the United States, show ages extending well past the close of the Pleistocene.

Ages obtained from a variety of locations are as follows (these are all in years before the present): 8,240 (Mead and Meltzer, 1984, p. 446); 7,000; 8,000 (Hester, 1960, p. 70); 6,160 (Marcus and Berger, 1984, p. 171); ~5,000 (Martin and Webb, 1974, p. 144); 3,800 (Schmidt, 1988, p. 253). A date of 2,167 B.C. was obtained based on horse bones from the northern part of the Yucatan Peninsula according to John L. Sorenson (Pers. Comm.).

Figure 18. Depiction of the Pleistocene horse, *Equus*, that was typical of those in North and Central America. Their fossils are among the most numerous of large mammals from this time. As indicated in both the Jaredite and Nephite records, the horse (and the ass) were useful to these peoples. Whether the horse and ass were found in the New World by the Jaredites, or brought over by them, is uncertain. Either scenario is possible. (The Nephites found these animals already here in the wilderness when they arrived). *(Figure by courtesy of the George C. Page Museum in southern California. John Dawson, artist. From Harris and Jefferson, 1985, "Treasures of the Tar Pits.")*

There is no question that by the close of the Pleistocene that the several species of horses and asses in the New World were dying out along with many other large mammals, based on the dwindling numbers of their fossils. Why? Scientists are not in accord as to the cause. One contingent argues that changing climatic conditions and environments were responsible. Another faction claims that as man became more populous, over-hunting by primitive peoples caused their demise. A third group, including myself, believe it was a combination of both factors. Nevertheless, small scattered populations of horse and ass, especially in remote areas, probably survived in North America until shortly before they were reintroduced by the Spaniards.[9] Some recent datings, mostly unpublished, lead me to this conclusion. The Carbon-14 dating involved was first instigated by Dr. Steven E. Jones, former physics professor at Brigham Young University. I later worked with him on these.

Some of the unpublished dates run on horse fossils that appear to be valid are: 5,890 B.C. (Pratt Cave in Texas); 830 B.C. (southern Saskatchewan, Canada); 815 A.D. (Ontario, Canada); 1,260-1,400 A.D. (Wolf Spider Cave, Colorado). A date of about 1,120 B.C. was determined using a thermoluminescence method on a horse bone from Horsethief Cave in Wyoming. While these dates are important, it will take a number of others in this age range to convince skeptics that the horse did continue in North America past the Pleistocene into historic times. In my opinion these dates eventually will come.

Reported dates less than 10,000 years before the present for horse fossils are unfortunately not yet common, but reports dis-

---

[9] It has not been entirely ruled out by some that a few very small herds of horses were possibly present in North America even at the time others were brought over from Europe. The same species brought over, *Equus caballus*, was native to both Europe and North America. These horses would easily have been able to interbreed, thus obscuring the native American horse that had remained.

cussing primitive man in association with the horse and ass in North America are. Many scientific articles have been written about this association in both North and Central America. Mesoamerica especially has a rich literature on this subject. Some of these articles date back to the 1800's (e.g., Heilprin, 1891; Mercer, 1896). Different species of *Equus* associated with man were reported by Mexican paleontologists Joaquin Arroyo-Cabrales and Oscar Polaco from several caves in the Yucatan Peninsula (2003, p. 273-288). A number of sites having a joint occurrence of horse and man have been reported throughout Mexico, though dates are often lacking (e.g., Irwin-Williams, 1967; MacNeish and Nelken-Terner, 1983; Pichardo, 2000b).

Archaeologist Mario Pichardo also wrote a review of the horses at Paleoindian sites in both North and South America (2004). He considered that there were eight species disseminated throughout these sites. It seems clear, at least to me, that the horses and asses, as well as the other animals listed in the Book of Mormon, were actually in America at the time they were said to be here. As given above, there is solid evidence in support of this. For additional information regarding the history of the horse, see Appendix B.

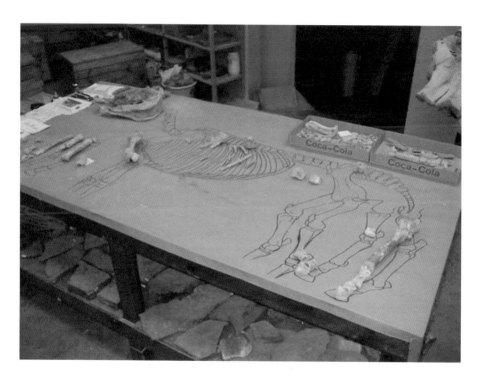

Figure 19. This is a partial reconstruction of a fossil horse the author recently helped collect in Mexico. *(Photo courtesy of Rosario Gómez, Directora de Paleontología. Coahuila, México.)*

13

Summation of Issues
in the
Book of Mormon

My mind is satisfied that all the items Joseph Smith translated as relating to the Book of Mormon actually existed in America as he transcribed them from the plates. This includes all the materials, plants and animals he stated were here. Many critics over the years have claimed that the Book of Mormon could not possibly be true, because it lists items that, "should not be in America" during the time indicated. However, scientific research has shown that many were in fact here when the Book of Mormon records that they were. Further scientific investigations continue to add supportive evidences.

While we cannot rely on science for all the answers that we would like relating to the scriptures, it has provided very important substantiating information. In the end, though, our testimonies of the truthfulness of the Book of Mormon must be built on faith in God. B. H. Roberts in writing about this very subject said, "Secondary evidences in support of truth, like secondary causes in natural phenomena [science], may be of firstrate importance, and mighty factors in the achievement of God's purposes."   "...The Holy Ghost must ever be the chief source of evidence for the truth of the Book of Mormon. All other evidence is secondary to this, the primary and infallible. No arrangement of evidence, however skillfully ordered; no argument, however adroitly made, can ever take its place." (1950, p. 7-8). I can only second his comments.

Appendix A

Impact of Fossils

Thomas Jefferson is well known as one of the founding fathers of the United States of America. A man of many accomplishments, he is also renowned for his keen intellect. However, few people realize his role in paleontology. Jefferson was one of the earliest men of note in our nation to give a scientific paper about a fossil. His paper concerned bones of the now extinct giant ground sloth (discussed in Chapter 11 of this book), and was presented before the American Philosophical Society of Philadelphia. It was published by this society in 1799. While ground sloths were not understood for what they were at the time, or even that they were actually extinct, Jefferson requested that Lewis and Clark be on the lookout for such a living beast on their famous expedition. As president, Jefferson maintained a modest collection of fossils in the White House. His collection also included many teeth and bones of mastodons. Lewis and Clark were told to search for this animal too, as Jefferson thought that the mastodon might still be living as well.

It was not until the latter part of the 18th Century and early part of the 19th Century, that most scientists came to agree on what fossils actually represented. Earlier than this it was thought that they were just "freaks of nature" as they were commonly called. Moreover, a majority of scientists during this time, often known as natural philosophers, were deeply religious. It was argued among them that to acknowledge fossils as extinct forms of life on earth, was to suggest that God was imperfect. The thinking was that if there were extinct life forms, then God's creations were not perfect, and therefore He could not be perfect either! This type of thinking of course was not just false, but it held back the progress of science. Only later in the 1800's were advances made in science relative to fossils and their true nature. They have conclusively been shown to represent ancient life on earth.

Many types of fossils have significantly helped to establish the earth's antiquity. They have also helped to date various geologic events such as when mountains and oceans formed. Fossils have given us a valuable window into the past, showing what types of life existed on earth, and when. Dinosaurs and other kinds of extinct organisms are only known from fossils. Fossil fuels are another very important aspect of past life on which we depend. They were certainly part of God's plan in providing for our needs.

My many years as a geologist/paleontologist have shown me that a number of unexpected finds of fossils in various rock layers, at different times, and in different parts of the world, have caused scientists to modify earlier held views. This is important because it relates to Book of Mormon animals and when they lived. There is no doubt, though, that many types of plants and animals that once lived on our earth are now extinct. Numerous examples could be provided. However, ones relating to Pleistocene (Ice Age) extinctions are those most relevant to animals mentioned in the Book of Mormon. It is important to keep in mind that when it comes to extinctions, new discoveries can change old beliefs.

Pleistocene extinctions are actually ones which are of importance regarding Book of Mormon peoples. This is because certain animals mentioned in this Book, and thought to have been extinct long before the period of time represented, might actually have survived until Book of Mormon peoples arrived in America. For many, many years paleontologists have been convinced that most of America's large mammals (along with certain other life forms) became extinct 10,000 to 12,000 years ago. Examples include the mammoth, mastodon, camel, horse, giant ground sloth, saber-tooth cat, and giant lion to name but a few. However, as more and more fossils have been found and dated, it has become clear that some of these animals lived on much longer than had previously been thought. At first these more recent ages, ones showing some animals lived on much longer than expected, were considered erroneous. They did not fit the established pattern.

Fortunately, science is about continually questioning and testing, and accepting new ideas when there is good evidence for them. Now there are many dates that have been run on certain extinct animals. These dates show that they lived long after the end of the Pleistocene, and more and more scientists are accepting these dates. Some of the ages obtained are not yet published, including ones where I have had a part. One which I have published involves two partial mastodon skeletons that were collected in Utah. The Carbon-14 age obtained for these animals show them to be close to 7,000 years old (Miller, 1987, p. 180). It is one of the youngest ages ever recorded for the American mastodon. Young as these mastodon fossils are by geological standards, they certainly would not have represented the last two living ones in America. And this holds true for any extinct species of any age.

What happens as unfavorable environmental conditions persist for plants and animals is that their numbers dwindle. In the case of Pleistocene mammals, changing conditions would cause them to seek areas still favorable to them, allowing them to survive there. As these areas became ever more restrictive, their numbers would continue to decrease. Finally a breeding population could no longer be maintained, and the species would then go extinct. Before extinction occurred, though, there would possibly be some individuals that might be fossilized. But the greatly reduced numbers of individuals would mean very few if any fossils would later be available for discovery[10]. They might go undetected for very long periods of time.

So it's certainly possible, even likely, that small populations of now extinct animals lived on for hundreds, or even thousands of years after the most recent fossil of their kind was dated. This helps explain why occasionally younger-aged fossils of a particular species are discovered. The fact that the last remaining animals of a given species would probably be living in a relatively small area (or areas) further diminishes the chance of finding their fossils. And finding a fossil that represents the last of its kind, would be millions of times less likely than winning the lottery! Nevertheless, with more and more searching for fossils, as is now going on at an accelerated rate, chances of finding rare fossils has improved. With this in mind, it should not be a surprise that Book of Mormon peoples could have known as well as tamed or domesticated now extinct animals.

---

[10] Examples of this situation occur at the famous Rancho La Brea Tar Pits in Los Angeles, California. I have studied many of the fossils from this site off and on for over 40 years. Although more than one million bones have been recovered from Rancho La Brea, only three are known from a single tapir. Just 12 bones represent a species of llama. Obviously these animals were not common to the immediate area, but nevertheless the evidence does show their presence there. If these few bones had not been found, it would have been thought that the tapir and llama did not exist here.

Appendix B

Horses in the Americas

It's interesting that of the many animals named or implied in the Book of Mormon, it is the horse that has drawn the most attention. From its first printing when the book was distributed throughout a small region of the eastern United States skeptics have used this familiar animal, the horse, as a means to discredit the Book as well as Joseph Smith.

Most critics have been of the opinion that the horse was unknown in the Americas before the Spaniards introduced it at the close of the 15th Century. Of his own knowledge, Joseph Smith could not have presumed that there were Precolumbian horses in America before his translation of the Book of Mormon from the gold plates. The fact that there were horses here before the second voyage of Columbus was not known to science until many years after the death of Joseph Smith.

Of necessity the story of the horse presented in this appendix is much abbreviated and simplified. It starts in North America. By the latter third of the 19th Century, paleontologists had come to realize that various kinds of horses existed on this continent. In fact they found out that the major history of the horse was preserved here as an essentially continuous record of multitudinous fossils, representing many millions of years. We now know that the first horses on earth appeared in North America. The story of their origin and development, though, has become more complex as additional fossils have been discovered. Ever expanding research over the past several decades has shown that there were more than 40 genera of horses, and many more species, living on this continent. They had adapted to a variety of environments. However, only one genus and a few species are all that remain as living forms on earth now.

Until recently paleontologists suggested that the earliest horse was one named *Hyracotherium* or *Eohippus* (two different names applied to the same genus; i.e., synonymous names). It is now believed by most researchers that two distinct genera are represented. The latter genus is thought to be the possible distant ancestor of the modern horse. *Hyracotherium,* though, appears to be ancestral to a separate, and now extinct, family of horse-like animals native to the Old World.

In the New World the true horse, *Eohippus,* was a small (about one foot tall at the shoulder), forest-dwelling animal. Its teeth show it was adapted to feed on leafy vegetation. The presumed forest environment is based on associated fossils, especially those of forest or woodland plants. Associated animals living with *Eohippus* include primates, deer-like types, primitive tapirs, primitive tree squirrels and many others, all well-suited to forest conditions. In addition, the physical characteristics of *Eohippus* and closely related genera imply this type of an environment that was made up of forests. These earliest horses had four toes on their front feet, and three on the hind feet, ideal for walking on a soft forest floor. Their fossils also show vestiges (splint bones) of additional digits, indicating an ancestor that had five toes in front and in back. The modern horse only has one toe front and back, with splint bones as mentioned in Chapter 7.

Unlike much earlier described scientific histories of the horse, this animal did not consist of just six or seven genera that led directly from *Eohippus* to our modern *Equus* through the Cenozoic Era. It is now known that there were many more genera of horses comprising the history of this animal. Although true horses were originally just in North America, the continued movement of the earth's crustal plates brought some continents into contact, which later separated.

This geologically brief contact allowed some animals, including the horse, to disperse into the Old World. Of course others from the Old World were able to come to the New World in this same manner. Fossils provide an interesting history of animal (and plant) dispersals throughout the world through time. These continental contacts enabled horses to move into Europe, Asia and Africa. In so far as Australia is concerned it was never in contact with any other continent during the time horses were developing, and therefore they were not present until introduced by man.

The horse did not gain access into South America until that previous island continent connected with North America in the Pliocene Epoch about 4.5 million years ago. This occurred when the Isthmus of Panama was first formed (Some of my own research, along with colleagues, has shown that this Isthmus first formed 1.5 million years earlier than was previously reported).

The reason why so many different kinds of horses existed in North America is also related to the movement of crustal plates, moving through different latitudes and hence different climate zones. These climatic zones were also affected by the forming of mountains which largely came about through plate collisions. Size and position of oceans were also affected.

All these changes of course helped to determine the types of climates, and hence vegetation, that would be present in an area. Like many (but not all) other animals, the horse adapted to a fairly wide range of habitats and vegetational zones. In general, though, the earth was becoming cooler and dryer throughout the Cenozoic Era (the last 65 million years of earth's history), the time horses were living on earth. With the cooling and drying, the vegetational zones changed.

Horses and other animals had to adapt, or else become extinct. Study of fossils clearly shows that both adaptations and extinctions occurred. With cooling and drying came extensive grasslands in temperate zones. Many animals adapted to this change, but many did not. The horses that were grazers did very well, but those that were browsers were the ones to become extinct. The one genus that survived, *Equus*, is the only genus now left on earth. All other genera, over 40, are extinct, known only by fossils.

The modern genus, *Equus*, though, is represented by several species. These include Asian wild horses, asses and zebras. In nature all are well suited to life on prairies or grasslands. Until the end of the Pleistocene Epoch, the horse was one of the best represented mammals in North America. Why it disappeared here in such a short time, still has paleontologists guessing. However, some recent research, not yet completed, suggests that horses might have survived in North America in limited numbers close to the time that they were re-introduced to the New World by Europeans. Reportedly, Columbus brought the first few horses to America on his second voyage in 1493. In following years Spaniards and others brought in more, both to North and South America. The fact that herds of horses now do well on these continents in the wild, makes their earlier disappearance more of a mystery.

References Cited

Adams, D. B. 1983. Last ditch archeology. *Science 83*, 4:28-37.

Agenbroad, L.D. 1984. New World mammoth distribution. *In*: P. S. Martin and R. G. Klein (eds.) *Quaternary Extinctions: A Prehistoric Revolution*, University of Arizona Press, Tucson, p. 90-108.

Arreano, A. R. V. 1951. Research in the continental Neogene of Mexico. *American Journal of Science*, 249:604-616.

Arroyo-Cabrales, J. and Alvarez, T. 2003. A preliminary report of the late Quaternary mammal fauna from Loltún Cave, Yucatán, México. *In*: B. W. Schubert, J. I. Mead and R. W. Graham (eds.) *Ice Age Faunas of North America,* Indiana University Press, Bloomington, p. 262-272.

Arroyo-Cabrales, J. and Johnson, E. 1995. A reappraisal of fossil vertebrates from San Josecito Cave, Nuevo Leon, Mexico. *In*: E. Johnson (ed.) *Ancient Peoples and Landscapes*, Museum of Texas Tech University, Lubbock, p. 217-231.

Arroyo-Cabrales, J. and Polaco, O. 2003. Caves and the Pleistocene vertebrate paleontology of Mexico. *In*: B. W. Schubert, J. I. Mead and R. W. Graham (eds.) *Ice Age Faunas of North America,* Indiana University Press, Bloomington, p. 273-291.

Asch, N. B. and D. L. 1985. Archeobotany. *In*: C. R. McGimsey and M. D. Conner (eds.) Deer Track: A late Woodland Village in the Mississippi Valley, *Center for American Archaeology,* Kampsville, Illinois, p. 79-82.

Ball, T. B. and Hess, W. M. 2004. Agriculture in Lehi's world: Some textual, historical, Archaeological, and botanical insights. *In*: J. W. Welch, D. R. and J. H. Seely (eds.) Glimpses of Lehi's Jerusalem, *Foundation for Ancient Research and Mormon Studies*, Brigham Young University, Provo, p. 149-191.

Benson, E. T. 1992. The keystone of our religion. *Ensign*, January, p. 2-7.

Bist, S. S., Cheeran, J. V., Choudhury, S., Baura, P. and Misra, M. K. 2001. The domesticated Asian elephant in India. *In*: I. Baker and M. Kashio (eds.) *Giants on Our Hands*, Proceedings of the International Workshop on the Domesticated Asian Elephant, Bankok, p. 129-148.

Carranza-Castañeda, O. and Miller, W. E. 1987. Rediscovered type specimens and other important published Pleistocene mammalian fossils from central Mexico. *Journal of Vertebrate Paleontology*, 7:335-341.

Carranza-Castañeda, O. and Miller, W. E. 2004. Late Tertiary terrestrial mammals from central Mexico and their relationship to South American immigrants. *Revista Brasileria de Paleontologia*, 7:249-261.

Colbert, E. H., Morales, M. and Minkoff, E. C. 2001. *Colbert's Evolution of the Vertebrates: A History of the Backboned Animals Through Time*. Wiley-Liss, New York, 560 pp.

Diamond, F. 1953. *The Story of Glass*. Harcourt, Brace and Company, New York, 246 pp.

Dott, R. H. and Batten, R. L. 1988. *Evolution of the Earth*. McGraw-Hill Book Company, New York, 643 pp.

Fisher, D. C. 1984. Mastodon butchering by North American Paleo-Indians. *Nature*, 308:271-272.

Forbes, R. J. 1950. *Metallurgy in Antiquity: A Notebook for Archaeologists and Technologists*. E. J. Brill, Leiden, Netherlands, 489 pp.

Frison, G. C., Walker, D. N., Webb, S. D. and Zeimens, G. M. 1978. Paleo-Indian procurement of *Camelops* on the northwestern plains. *Quaternary Research*, 10:385-400.

Furlong, E. L. 1925. Notes on the occurrence of mammalian remains in the Pleistocene of Mexico, with a description of a new species, *Capromeryx mexicana*. *University of California Publications in Geological Sciences*. 15:137-152.

García-Bárcena, J. 1989. El hombre y los proboscideos de America. *In*: L. Mirambell (ed.), *Homenaje a José Luis Lorenzo*, Instituto Nacional de Antropología e Historia, Mexico City, p. 41-101.

Gill, R. B. 2000. *The Great Maya Droughts: Water, Life, and Death*. University of New Mexico Press, Albuquerque, 464 pp.

Glowiak, E. M. and Rowland, S. M. 2003. Did Clovis hunters butcher Pleistocene mammals at Gypsum Cave, Nevada? *Geological Society of America, Abstracts with Programs*, 35:498.

Graham, R. W., Haynes, C. V., Johnson, D. L. and Kay, M. 1981. Kimmswick: H Clovis-mastodon association in eastern Missouri. *Science*, 213:1115-1117.

Hall, E. R. and Kelson, K. R. 1959. *The Mammals of North America*. Ronald Press Company, New York, 1,083 pp.

Harrington, M. R. 1933. Gypsum Cave, Nevada. *Southwest Museum Papers*, 8:1-197.

Harris, J. M. 1985. Treasures of the Tar Pits. *Natural History Museum of Los Angeles County. Science Series* 31, Los Angeles, 87 pp.

Hatt, R. T. 1953. Faunal and archeological researches in Yucatan caves. *Cranbrook Institute of Science*, 33:1-42.

Heilprin, A., 1891. Geological researches in Yucatan. *Proceedings of the Academy of Natural Sciences of Philadelphia*, 42:136-158.

Hess, W. M. 2008. Personal Communication.

Hester, J. J. 1960. Late Pleistocene extinction and radiocarbon dating. *American Antiquity*, 26:58-77.

Irwin-Williams, C. 1967. Associations of early man with horse, camel and mastodon at Hueyatlaco, Valsequillo (Puebla, Mexico). *In*: P.S. Martin and H. E. Wright (eds.) *Pleistocene Extinctions, the Search for a Cause*, Yale University Press, New Haven, p. 337-347.

Jefferson, T. 1799. A memoir of the discovery of certain bone of a quadruped of the clawed kind in the western parts of Virginia. *American Philosophical Society Transactions, 4:246-260.*

Johnson, L. H. 1952. Men and elephants in America. *The Scientific Monthly*, 75:215-221.

Kalb, J. E. and Mebrate, A. 1993. Fossil elephantoids from the hominid-bearing Awash Group, Middle Awash Valley, Afar Depression, Ethiopia. *American Philosophical Society Transactions*, 83:1-114.

Keegan, J. 1993. *A History of Warfare*. Alfred A. Knopf, Inc. New York, 432 pp.

Kowallis, B. J. 1998. In the Thirty and Fourth year: A geologist's view of the great destruction in 3 Nephi. *Brigham Young University Stu*dies, 37:137-190.

Kurtén, B. and Anderson, E. 1980. *Pleistocene Mammals of North America*. Columbia University Press, New York, 442 pp.

Latcham, R. E. 1922. Los Animales domésticos de la América precolombiana. *Museo de Etnología y Antropología de Chile*, 3:1-199.

Lev-Yaden, S., Gopher, A. and Abbo, S. 2000. The cradle of agriculture. *Science*, 288:1602-1603.

Lucas, S. G. and González-León, C. 1997. *Cuvieronius* (Mammalia, Proboscidea) de Oquitoa, Sonora. *Geologia del Noroeste*, 2:12-13.

MacFadden, B. J. 1992. *Fossil Horses: Systematics, Paleobiology, and Evolution of the Family Equidae*. Cambridge University Press, New York, 369 pp.

Macfarlane, A. and Martin, G. 2002. *Glass, a World History*. University of Chicago Press, Chicago, 255 pp.

MacNeish, R. S, and Nelken-Terner, A. 1983. The preceramic of Mesoamerica. *Journal of Field Archaeology*, 10:71-84.

Marcus, L. F. and Berger, R. 1984. The significance of radiocarbon dates for Rancho La Brea. *In*: P. S. Martin and R. G. Klein (eds.) *Quaternary Extinctions: A Prehistoric Revolution*, University of Arizona Press, Tucson, p. 159-183..

Martin, P. S. 2005. *Twilight of the Mammoths*. University of California Press, Berkeley, 250 pp.

Martin, R. A. and Webb, S. D. 1974. Late Pleistocene mammals from the Devil Den fauna, Levy County, Florida. *In*: S. D. Webb (ed.) *Pleistocene Mammals of Florida*. The University Presses of Florida, p. 114-145.

Matheny, R. T. 2008. Personal Communication.

Mead, J. I., Haynes, C. V. and Huckell, B. B. 1979. A late Pleistocene mastodon (*Mammut americanum*) from the Lehner site, southeastern Arizona. *The Southwestern Naturalist*, 24:231-238.

Mead, J. I. and Meltzer, D. J. 1984. North American late Quaternary extinctions and the radiocarbon record. *In*: P. S. Martin and R. G. Klein (eds.) *Quaternary Extinctions: A Prehistoric Revolution*, University of Arizona Press, Tucson, p. 440-450.

Mercer, H. C. 1896. *The Hill Caves of Yucatan; a Search for evidence of man's antiquity in the caverns of Central America, being an account of the Corwith Expedition of the Department of Archaeology and Paleontology of the University of Pennsylvania*. J. B. Lippincott, Philadelphia, 183 pp.

Miller, W. E. 1987. *Mammut americanum*, Utah's first record of the American mastodon. *Journal of Paleontology*, 61:168-183.

Miller, W. E. 2002. Quaternary vertebrates of the northeastern Bonneville Basin and vicinity of Utah. *In*: J. W. Gwynn (ed.) *Great Salt Lake: An Overview of Change*. Special Publication of the Utah Department of Natural Resources. Salt Lake City, p. 54-69.

Miller, W. E. and Carranza-Castañeda, O. 2001. Late Cenozoic mammals from the basins of Central Mexico. *Bollettino della Society Paleontologica Italiana*, 40:235-242.

Montellano-Ballesteros, M. 2002. New *Cuvieronius* finds from the Pleistocene of Central Mexico. *Journal of Paleontology*, 76:578-583.

Nibley, H. 1988. *Since Cumorah*. Deseret Book Company, Salt Lake City, and Brigham Young University, *Foundation for Ancient Research and Mormon Studies*, Provo, 512 pp.

Osborn H. F. 1942. *Proboscidea*. American Museum of Natural History Press, New York, 2:805-1676.

Pichardo, M. 2000a. Redating Iztapan and Valsequillo, Mexico. *Radiocarbon*, 42:305-310.

Pichardo, M. 2000b. Valsequillo biostratigraphy III: Equid ecospecies in Paleoindian sites. *Anthropologischer Anzeiger Jahrgang*, 3:275-298.

Pichardo, M. 2001. Valsequillo biostratigraphy IV: Proboscidean ecospecies in Paleoindian sites. *Anthropologischer Anzeiger Jahrgang*, 59:41-60.

Pichardo, M. 2004. Review of horses in Paleoindian sites of the Americas. *Anthropologischer Anzeiger Jahrgang*, 62:11-35.

Prado, J. L., Alberti, M. T., Azanza, B., Sánchez, B. and Frassinetti, D. 2001. The Pleistocene gomphotheres (Proboscidea) from South America: Diversity, habitats and feeding ecology. *In*: G. Cavarretta, P. Giola, M. Mussi and M. R. Palombo (eds.) *The World of Elephants*, 1st International Congress, Roma, Italy, p. 337-340.

Prothero, D. R. 2007. *Evolution: What the Fossils Say and Why it Matters*. Columbia University Press, New York, 381 pp.

Roberts, B. H. 1950 (originally written in 1909) *New Witness for God*. Deseret Book Company, Salt Lake City, 501 pp.

Romer, A. S. 1929. A fresh skull of an extinct American camel. *Journal of Geology*, 37:261-267.

Schmidt, P. J. 1988. La entrada del hombre a la Península de Yucatán. *In*: J. Gonzáles (ed.) *Origenes del Hombre Amerícano (Seminario)*, Secretaría de Educación Pública, México, p. 245-261.

Shipman, P., Fisher, D. C. and Rose, J. J. 1984. Mastodon butchery: Microscopic evidence of carcass processing and bone tool use. *Paleobiology*, 10:358-365.

Sorenson, J. L. 1985. *An Ancient American Setting for the Book of Mormon*. Deseret Book Company, Salt Lake City, 415 pp.

Sorenson, J. L. 1992. *Animals in the Book of Mormon*: An Annotated Bibliography., Foundation for Ancient Research and Mormon Studies, Brigham Young University, Provo, 55 pp.

Sorenson, J. L. 1995. A new evaluation of the Smithsonian Institution statement regarding the Book of Mormon. Unpublished report, 21 pp.

Sorenson, J. L. and Johannessen, C. L. 2006. Biological evidence for Pre-columbian transoceanic voyages. *In*: V. H. Mair (ed.) *Contact and Exchange in the Ancient World,* University of Hawaii Press, Honolulu, p. 238-297.

Sorenson, J. L. 2007. Personal Communication.

Stokes, W. L. 1972. Probable proboscidean petroglyphs of southeastern Utah. *Utah Academy Proceedings*, 49:84-85.

Walker, E. P., Warnick, F., Hamlet, S. E., Lange, K. I., Davis, M. A., Uible, H. E. and Wright. P. F. 1968. The Camelidae. *In*: J. L. Paradiso (ed.) *Mammals of the World*: *The Camelidae*, Johns Hopkins Press, Baltimore, p. 1371-1377.

Webb, S. D. 1974. Pleistocene llamas of Florida, with a brief review of the Lamini. *In*: S. D. Webb (ed.) *Pleistocene Mammals of Florida*, University of Florida Press, Gainsville, p. 170-213.

Wheeler, J. 2003. Evolution and origin of the domestic camelids. *Rocky Mountain Llama and Alpaca Association*, ILR report, 8:1-14.

Yesner, D. R., Veltre, D. W., Crossen, K J. and Graham, R. W. 2005. 5,700 year-old mammoth remains from Qagnax Cave, Priblof Islands, Alaska. *In*: L. D. Agenbroad and R. L. Symington (eds.) *The World of Elephants:* Short Papers and Abstracts of the 2nd International Congress, p. 200-204.

About the Author

(Photo courtesy of Robert Moore)

Wade E. Miller

Wade E. Miller, Ph.D., is a retired professor of geology at Brigham Young University. He served as Chairman of the Geology Department for three terms and as Director of the Earth Science Museum at BYU. Additionally he was Sigma Xi lecturer in recognition of his achievements in science at the University.

For more than forty years Dr. Miller has done extensive research in geology and paleontology. This has taken place in the field as well as in the laboratory. He is currently active on a number of field projects in the western United States as well as in Mexico. Wade Miller has been involved in research at museums in the United States, Canada, Mexico, England, Germany, and Japan. He has also been a paleontological advisor to several museums, as well as to the Bureau of Land Management in the United States. Additionally he has served on various committees for professional organizations including the National Science Foundation, and the Governor's board for paleontology in the state of Utah.

In the area of Book of Mormon research, Dr. Miller has made a special study of items mentioned in the Book of Mormon that have caused many critics to question its veracity. His book hopefully sets to rest many of the arguments posed by these critics.

Wade Miller is a noted writer of more than 75 articles on paleontology and geology. He has also appeared on a variety of television shows including Good Morning America, and The Today Show, in addition to participating in several documentaries about fossils. One of these was A&E's "Dinosaur!" narrated by Walter Cronkite. As an internationally recognized authority of life of the past, Dr. Miller has been an invited lecturer in the United States, Mexico, Brazil, Italy and Japan. He has also presented many firesides and lectures on life of the past and the creation of the earth to LDS church audiences in the United States, Mexico, and Italy.

As a member of the LDS Church, Brother Miller has held a number of callings, including serving in three bishoprics, one of them as a bishop. He and his wife, Patricia, have three sons and five grandchildren.

Made in the USA
Lexington, KY
11 June 2014